Q I:

THE QUEST
FOR INTELLIGENCE

KEVIN WARWICK

PIATKUS

Copyright © 2000 by Kevin Warwick

Published in the UK in 2000 by
Judy Piatkus (Publishers) Limited
5 Windmill Street
London W1T 2JA
e-mail: info@piatkus.co.uk

This paperback edition published in 2001

The moral right of the author has been asserted

*A catalogue record for this book is available
from the British Library*

ISBN 0 7499 2081 5 Hbk
ISBN 0 7499 2230 3 Pbk

Page design by Zena Flax

Typeset by Wyvern 21, Bristol
Printed and bound in Great Britain by
Mackays of Chatham Limited

CONTENTS

ACKNOWLEDGEMENTS

Intelligence is, I feel, the most significant aspect of any individual's existence. Its importance is paramount, yet it is a subject about which humans appear to know little and hold more prejudices and biases than any other. I hope this book will not only give a greater awareness of our own intelligence, acknowledging the differences that exist, but also a deeper appreciation of the intelligence of non-humans, particularly machines.

No book such as this can be completed successfully without the help and support of one's family. My wife Irena has often helped to discuss and criticise the contents, frequently when she was trying to do something else, and at least once in the middle of the night. My children Maddi and James have been super-critical throughout, and my step-daughter Lenka talked through some of the sections with me. I have also, for the last twelve years, considered those in the Department of Cybernetics at Reading University to be part of my family. Chief amongst these, Iain Goodhew has been my travelling companion to Paris, Moscow and elsewhere. Back home, Darren

Wenn, Jim Wyatt, Paul Minchinton, Chris Smith, Rak Patel, Mark Gasson, Neil Glover, Iain Werry, Julian Brooker, Ben Hutt and many others have done far more for me than I could ever expect of normal humans.

Some people have been extremely helpful in enabling me, through discussion, to focus the ideas presented here. For their help I would like to thank (in no particular order) Gary Kasparov, Marvin Minsky, John Searle, Mark Bishop, Roger Penrose, Richard Gregory, Susan Greenfield, Michael Behar and some old guy I met once on the train up to Sheffield. Robert Kirby, my agent, did a marvellously annoying job of focusing the work early on.

Whilst I thank all those above I would also like to mention Liz Lucas and Carole Leppard, who have provided secretarial input, Sheila Gainey, who carried out a beach-combing exercise on the news, Louise Parlett who helped to target and draw out the original contents list and the students of Reading University who willingly took part in the IQ study in Chapter 7. I would also like to extend my gratitude to Elma, Walter, Hissing Sid, Gershwyn, Cyberhand, the Dalek, and the Seven Dwarfs: all robots that have assisted considerably by performing when asked!

My sincere and heartfelt thanks, however, go to Claire Whitehead. Over the last thirty months she has acted as researcher, drafter, critic and editor on the book. Without her this book would certainly not have been completed.

Kevin Warwick
Reading
July 2000

INTRODUCTION

HUMANS ARE, WITHOUT DOUBT, the dominant species on earth. We are the only creatures who have explored, and can exist in, virtually all regions of the world, and who have even, in the last few decades, continued our explorations beyond our own planet. What is it about us that makes this dominance possible? There are certainly many other creatures who are faster and stronger than us, so how have we gained this pre-eminent position? The only sensible answer to this question must be our intelligence.

As our intelligence is so critical to our success, surely we should have a clear idea of what being an intelligent individual entails. Amazingly, this is not the case. Despite years of research and argument no universal definition has ever been decided upon. Even worse, many attempts to define it have been, and indeed still are, so riddled with bias as to be laughable: in the last thirty years, the measure of an individual's intelligence has been used as the basis for loss of freedom, the removal of sexual reproductive ability, and even death.

It is now vitally important that a true definition of intelligence should be agreed upon. For the last decade I have been deeply involved in research into how robots think, and why they behave in the ways they do. In my previous book *March of the Machines* I presented conclusions from this research, stating that in years to come robots will be more intelligent than our own species. The consequences of this for humans are dire. If we allow the robots of the future to be more intelligent than ourselves it is they, not us, who will dominate the earth. How can we possibly stop this from happening if we cannot agree on what intelligence is in the first place? We must, I feel, fully investigate this subject in order to ensure our own survival.

You personally may believe that the idea of super-intelligent robots taking over the world is pure fantasy, but if we continue to ignore present warning signs it *will* happen. It is important to realise that robots can be individuals themselves, and that they can be no more 'programed' than you or I. They can, even now, learn from their environment and react to features within it, so what might they do in the future? Perhaps even more disturbing and exciting is the latest research I have become involved in – the possibility of developing cyborgs. Imagine what a part human, part machine entity could accomplish; how powerful a cyborg would be when the two different 'mental' processes, human and machine, are combined.

In 1998, in the first of a series of experiments, I took some tentative steps towards beginning this culture of cyborgs when I had a silicon chip transponder surgically implanted in my left arm. This experiment, and its results, are described in full, for the first time, within this book. Further experiments are ongoing, and the direction in which they are heading is quite shocking. In the pages that follow I will describe the astounding future that I believe lies before us, including the possibility of humans communicating by thought alone.

———

My quest is to find out what intelligence is all about. This book describes that quest. As the pages unfold, your views and values will receive a severe jolt: for the first time, the intelligence of humans will be directly compared with that of animals, insects and robots.

Many of your present ideas about intelligence will, I am convinced, be turned on their heads when you read about some of the incredible things that animals and robots can now do. Perhaps you will, as a result, feel that you personally are a lot more intelligent than you previously thought. You will certainly see your own mental abilities in a new light.

We are humans and we can only view the world in terms of our own senses and values. We cannot fully comprehend the world from an insect or robot viewpoint because we do not have their brain and senses. However, we certainly should not belittle or dismiss the way others behave because we do not understand them.

In this book the concept of Subjective Intelligence is presented. This is central to an understanding of intelligence; without it we can have no hope of getting to grips with what intelligence really is. As a comparative measure, the Hypersphere of Intelligence is also introduced. This revolutionary idea allows us to directly compare the intelligence of a human with that of an insect or robot.

In addition, the Intelligence Hypershape of an individual is introduced and fully explained. You will be able to work out your own Hypershape and compare it with mine.

Many readers will be keen to learn how best to improve short-term intellectual performance in order to do well in an examination or interview. For example, does food and drink affect our intelligence? Should we watch television, read books or take exercise? Specifically for the purposes of this book, an experiment was carried out on a series of human volunteers. The dramatic and surprising results presented here give a clear guidance as to what to do immediately before an examination in order to maximise your performance. It will also tell you what *not* to do if you wish to avoid failure.

It is imperative for our future that we gain a much clearer understanding of intelligence in humans, animals and machines. Many old wives' tales and unsubstantiated theories need to be thrown out, to be replaced by scientific evidence. This book contains such evidence.

———

Machines have increasingly become part of human life, assisting us both physically and mentally. Physically, they can move objects that we would otherwise have no hope of moving and travel at speeds that we would otherwise have no hope of travelling at. Mentally, they can process and store huge amounts of data at rapid speeds, which human brainpower alone would have no chance of dealing with.

When this machine intelligence is working *for humans* there is no problem. But surely machines which can think for themselves, and are intelligent in their own right, will eventually cause us problems. Certainly, if they are far more intelligent than we are, will it still be possible for us to call the shots? If not, perhaps we are facing the prospect of a world run by machines rather than humans.

At this point you may be saying, 'Yes, but machines will never be . . .' with words like 'conscious', 'self-aware', 'creative' or perhaps 'emotional' filling the gap. But are you *sure* they won't be? The fact is that we already have machines that exhibit all these characteristics. In this book I have attempted to give a clear explanation of what it means for a machine to be intelligent – including all those aspects mentioned above, commonly believed to be confined to humans.

It is human mental agility and our unique thought processes which make up our intelligence, and it is our intelligence which is the key to our power. Surely, then, it is dangerous to produce machines that can outstrip us mentally. In the later chapters the question of whether machine intelligence will overtake human intelligence is thrashed out.

In order to ascertain whether humans are really in a delicate situation we need to look at what actually constitutes intelligence. Numerous measures, numbers and quotients have been used to indicate the extent or level of intelligence. But can these measures be applied to animals and machines as well as humans? Is it possible to accurately measure and quantify human intelligence compared with that of other beings? If not, perhaps we will be unable to fully appreciate the evolutionary threat posed by machine intelligence until it is too late.

Because of their huge intellect, machines can actually be far more creative than humans. For example, they can design new systems or computer programs that humans have little chance of even comprehending, let alone defending themselves against.

This book explores exactly what we mean by intelligence. What is it about human intelligence that differentiates us from animals and machines? It is only by understanding what is *really* of value in human intelligence that we will have any hope of surviving.

1

DEFINING INTELLIGENCE – AN IMPOSSIBLE TASK

INTELLIGENCE IS A TERM WE ALL think we understand, but do we? What do we mean when we describe someone, some animal or even some thing, as being intelligent?

The human species has been evolving, both physically and mentally, for over a million years. Over the last two centuries, however, our environment and culture have undergone a process of rapid change. These changes have had a profound impact on the way we live and the way we think.

Enormous demands are placed on the human brain today. With the advent of modern communication systems, people on either side of the world can communicate instantly. Modern transport systems enable us to make journeys, which in the past took months, in a matter of hours.

Now, at the dawn of the twenty-first century, we are approaching a moment of crucial self-evaluation. Changes in the mental and physical abilities of humans, animals and machines have prompted a dramatic shift in the way we view intelligence. Is it still true, even now, to say that humans are the most intelligent entities on the planet?

PREVIOUS ATTEMPTS TO DEFINE INTELLIGENCE

The quest for the source of intelligence is currently a hot topic amongst scientists. Ours is a civilisation in flux, but what kind of society do we want for our children? For the first time in our evolutionary history, we are close to having the biological understanding, the economic ability and the cultural willpower to change the intelligence of future generations, but first we need to know what intelligence is.

The *New English Dictionary*, published in 1932, defined it as: 'The exercise of understanding: intellectual power: acquired knowledge: quickness of intellect.' This definition focused on knowledge and mental speed in themselves as being indications of intelligence. However, a typical modern-day definition (taken from the 1995 edition of the *Macmillan Encyclopaedia*) states, 'Intelligence is the ability to reason and to profit by experience. An individual's level of intelligence is determined by a complex interaction between their heredity and environment.'

One of the clearest statements on the subject was made by Binet (inventor of the IQ test) and a fellow researcher in the early 1900s: 'It seems to us that there is a fundamental faculty in intelligence, any alteration or lack of which is of the utmost importance for practical life. This is judgement, otherwise known as common sense, practical sense, initiative, the ability to adapt oneself to circumstance. To judge well, to comprehend well, to reason well, these are the essential ingredients of intelligence.'

However, we could easily fill an entire book with different definitions of intelligence, some mere variations on those just given, others radically different. It would seem that what is considered a vitally important component of intelligence by one person may not be considered so by another.

There is, in essence, no widely accepted – universal – definition of intelligence. Every attempt to define it has had its critics. This is because intelligence is an entity which is not clearly visible, and cannot be easily measured. Any definition is based solely on the beliefs and experiences of the individual who suggests it, and it is therefore bound to be criticised by those with different backgrounds and beliefs.

In recent years intelligence has been linked with such diverse factors as spiritual awareness,[1] or emotions.[2] In the latter case, intangible characteristics (such as social deftness, persistence and empathy) are regarded as critical aspects of an individual's intelligence, even though they may not be quantifiable. It is difficult to see what relevance these concepts have outside the context of human interaction.

In my role as Cybernetics Professor at Reading University I have had the opportunity to study not only humans, other animals and insects, but also robots. The robots in the Cybernetics laboratories can learn, communicate with each other, hunt for prey, and exhibit individual behaviours and characteristics. So, what of their intelligence? How does it compare with that of an insect or a human? Does the modern-day definition of intelligence quoted earlier apply to all creatures including robots? To answer these questions, we need to explore the characteristics of intelligence.

Robots we have built for a special robot pit at the Science Museum, London, act as predators and chase after their victim, or conversely try to escape. Does this mean they are angry or scared? If humans or animals acted this way we would assume that they felt anger or fear, so should we think the same of robots? The robots can also carry out a co-ordinated dance routine. Bees can do the same. So is a human dancer showing any special ability?

CHALLENGING PRECONCEPTIONS ABOUT INTELLIGENCE

It is important to realise that intelligence is an integral part of an individual's make up. It is dependent not only on that individual's brain but also on how that individual can sense the world and activate things in it. In most animals a single brain is connected to a nervous system which sends and receives signals as part of a body. How the world is perceived by an individual depends on the capabilities and functioning of their brain, their senses and even their actuators (muscles in humans).

Do humans have ultraviolet or x-ray senses? Not that we know of. All sorts of things could be happening at the ultrasonic level and a human would not be bothered by them at all. Yet the same signals could cause a bat or a robot endless problems. A being's senses have to be taken into account when considering intelligence. A human is merely one type of being. Just because another being is not the same as us in some way, this does not automatically make them worse. In fact it could easily make them better.

The success of a species depends on it 'performing well' (surviving and producing offspring) in its own particular environment. And intelligence plays a critical part in this success. As we will see, in Chapters 10 and 11, creatures such as apes, parrots, ants and bees all succeed brilliantly in their own way. We should not therefore regard ourselves as the only intelligent creatures on earth, but open up our concepts of intelligence to encompass the abilities of other creatures. For example, how many of our so-called 'human' characteristics, such as social deftness and persistence, are also possessed by these other creatures? How many apparently 'highly intelligent' human acts can be performed better by robots?

For humans, an individual's intelligence is inextricably linked to the relative importance played by society on that individual's abilities. What is, and what is not, intelligence therefore depends on the definitions employed by society. For example, why do we tend to regard a theoretical physicist such as Albert Einstein as more intelligent than a hamburger vendor? As you read this book, I hope that your concept of intelligence will broaden. Perhaps it will give you a greater appreciation of a wasp's thought patterns, the decision problems faced by a learning robot, or the way a person with autism responds to a situation. Perhaps, as a result, you will even start to believe that the hamburger vendor could well outstrip Einstein in some areas.

Distinguishing between Knowledge and Intelligence

Most of us tend to have very entrenched ideas about what is and what is not intelligent behaviour. These ideas of intelligence, more often than not, relate to activities in which we ourselves excel, and likewise we tend to put a low value on abilities outside our own range of performance. If it is not something we can do well, or can see much sense in, it is generally regarded as an act requiring little or no intelligence.

Our range of performance is dictated by a number of factors, including our language, our cultural background, and the knowledge we have acquired. But do these factors have anything to do with our intelligence? To illustrate the problem, consider this question from an actual IQ test:

'Which is the odd one out? Dickens, Wells, Einstein, Defoe, Swift.'[3]

The answer to this is Einstein, the theoretical physicist, the others all being British writers. Clearly knowledge of literature and science is required to answer the question, which is steeped in a particular culture and tradition. But why is it assumed that knowledge of the correct answer gives an indication of intelligence in any individual? Is someone who has never heard of Jonathan Swift less intelligent than someone who has heard of him? I do not believe so.

Now look at this question, which is based on my own cultural experience:

'Which is the odd one out? Porterfield, Branfoot, Hislop, McGee.'

To the majority of people who read this book these names may not be familiar. But to any ardent supporter of Reading Football Club they should be well known. The odd one out is Shaka Hislop, who used to play in goal for Reading, while the other three are past managers.

Clearly, for the group of people who can be classified as Reading supporters the question would seem easy, while others would find it totally mystifying. This football example is, however, only one step on from the literature example previously cited. Can we draw the same conclusions and say that those who got this answer right are more intelligent than those who did not? Of course not.

It has long been widely accepted that those people who are knowledgeable about the arts, classical music and literature are more intelligent than those who are not. If, however, we look at the two sample questions in more depth we can see that both require the ability to store, and repeat on demand, certain pieces of information. Is it really fair to say that the ability to do this with facts concerning literature makes you more intelligent than does the ability to recall facts based on sporting knowledge?

THE SUBJECTIVE THEORY OF INTELLIGENCE

Using these examples we can get to the real root of the problem – intelligence is subjective in terms of the group by which it is being viewed. For any group, indications of intelligence are steeped in the social and cultural trappings of its members. This means that those interested in literature consider in-depth knowledge of classical authors and their novels to be far more important, on the scale of intelligence, than knowledge of footballing facts, while those inter- ested in football would hold the opposite view. We can see from this that intelligence tests are always going to be biased towards the authors' beliefs, interests and experiences. If an individual sitting the test has opposing views, or comes from a very different background, they are never going to do well, whether or not they are highly intelligent.

Every individual has their own concept of what makes up intel- ligence. For some, social behaviour may be most important; for oth- ers it is mathematical skill or abstract reasoning; while others may see historical knowledge as a key factor. Each of us has our own set of beliefs as to what constitutes intelligent behaviour. This means that within any group of people we will find subgroups who have some ideas in common. For example, if we take a literature group there could be a subdivision who believe that one particular author is the best and knowledge of his work shows intelligence. This group may be further pared down to people who have an extensive interest in one particular novel by this author. This subdividing can theoretically continue until we get to an individual perspective. This is subjective intelligence taken to its logical extreme – intelligence as seen by the individual.

Let us look at this extreme case. As an individual, I can set a test of intelligence based on my own knowledge and experience. Consider the following questions:

In each case, which is the odd one out?

1. Newcastle	Oxford	London	Cambridge
2. BSc	MSc	PhD	DSc
3. Sheila	Susan	Sarah	Sonia
4. Australia	India	USA	Russia

Assuming that knowledge of my life is an indication of intelligence, a really intelligent person should score 4 out of 4.

So how did you do? The answers are as follows:

1. Cambridge – The university in which I have never held a post.

2. MSc – the qualification I do not have.

3. Sonia – I have never kissed a girl by that name.

4. Australia – I have never been there.

Unless you were me, know me very well, or were very lucky, it is unlikely that you scored more than 1 out of 4. Does that mean you are not intelligent? In reality no, but in terms of my test yes. In fact, if I set a number of such tests only one conclusion can be drawn: *I* am the most intelligent person on earth. This is subjective intelligence.

It is of course ridiculous to measure the intelligence level of an individual by means of this test, but in reality how different is it from more traditional intelligence tests? IQ tests, which we have all at some time taken, may not use personal experience to the extent my test has done, but they certainly do not manage to exclude the influence of cultural and social beliefs and experiences. This is why the results of such intelligence tests will always favour people of the same background as the test producer – the tests are inevitably biased and subjective.

THE IMPLICATIONS OF SUBJECTIVE INTELLIGENCE

We are not only subjective in the way we view other human beings' intelligence, but also in our assessment of animal and machine intelligence. We all have preconceived ideas, despite clear evidence to the contrary. For example, many people think pigs are dirty, smelly animals and as a consequence not very intelligent. This is patently untrue – pigs are, when compared to other animals, of relatively high intelligence. Likewise, many people think machines have no intelligence at all, that they get things done by following programs. This again is not true; some can learn and adapt, and such abilities are growing with every technological advancement made.

So, each individual has their own framework of intelligence which they impose on others in order to make comparisons. A group view of intelligence arises from consensus between individuals who hold certain social and cultural beliefs and assumptions in common. Everyone's framework reflects their own personal qualities, pandering to the universal desire to be the best.

———

Intelligence has many aspects, and to even attempt to measure it successfully we need to look at one aspect at a time. In the case of most machines at present, this is perhaps not such a difficult task. But in humans, where do we start? What is the most important facet to examine? To be fair to all people, it should be based on inherent mental abilities, as opposed to applied, resultant abilities. But how can such features be measured?

The aim of this book is to try to get as close as possible to an ultimate answer to the question of intelligence. Animals, insects and machines will all be considered, but the main subject will be humans. After all, being human, we know most about human intelligence. But how did our intelligence develop? Is our brain size linked to our intelligence? How and why did ancient civilisations create such extraordinary artefacts? All these questions and more are investigated in the next chapter.

2

HUMAN EVOLUTION AND INTELLIGENCE

WE TEND TO CONSIDER HUMAN INTELLIGENCE in terms of the present, the near future, or the recent past. In the present we are often concerned with one individual's intelligence compared with another. In the future we hope to become more intelligent, maybe through the use of technology. And history, or the past, allows us to learn from the mistakes made by our predecessors. However, none of these areas of discussion gives us any clues as to what intelligence actually *is* or *where* it came from. Perhaps the answers lie in our evolution as a species.

By looking for evidence of human intelligence in the archaeological record, we may be able to trace its development through our evolution. Have we always, even from the dawn of human existence, had the ability to out-perform other species? Or did some unspecified 'event' take place which changed the way our ancestors thought?

And can the history of ancient societies, such as those of the Aztecs and Incas, shed any light on how our intelligence has developed?

Brain Capacity and Intelligence

Our evolution as a species began around ten to five million years ago with the appearance of the Australopithecines (an ape-like hominid). Our own species, *Homo sapiens*, did not arrive till 100,000 years ago, following a number of other species.

A number of points arise from any investigation of our evolution. Most importantly there are the changes in brain capacity that occurred in the transition from one species to the next. Without doubt, these physical changes in brain size must have some bearing on the development of intelligence. Several other aspects may also be relevant: tool use, dietary changes and other physical developments. But can the birth of human intelligence really be put down to a simple evolutionary change?

The brain capacity of our ancestors changed from a mere 400 cubic centimetres in Australopithecines to a far larger 1370 cubic centimetres (average) in our own species. This change was not a slow, steady, gradual progression. Instead it seems to have occurred in a number of specific identifiable expansions. Importantly, this brain expansion is not in evidence among *any* other mammal species. So it was not just part of a general mammalian trend.[1]

The first occurrence of brain expansion seems to coincide with the arrival of the earliest *Homo* species, and appears to be related to the development of stone tool industries. The second is placed somewhere between 500,000 and 100,000 years ago, and is often associated with the appearance of *Homo sapiens*.[2]

It is this later expansion which is the most interesting in the context of our present investigation. It is characterised not only by an increase in brain size but also involves a drastic reshaping of the neurocranium (the brain casing), including dimensional modifications in the frontal and occipital bones. These morphological changes are particularly remarkable because they occurred over such a relatively short period of time.

However, this second episode of expansion is also extremely puzzling because it is not accompanied by any identifiable change in the archaeological record. Does this indicate that there was no concurrent change in intellectual behaviour? If so, what significance does brain size have in relation to intelligence?

Many of us tend to assume that the bigger the brain, the 'brainier' (and more intelligent) the person is. This being the case, it is surprising to discover that Neanderthal man (*Homo neanderthalensis*) – an earlier hominid species often portrayed as thuggish and stupid – had a brain capacity somewhere between 1200 and 1750 cubic centimetres,[3] a figure the same if not greater than our own.

Research has shown that life for Neanderthals was far from simple. How, then, did they survive for so long – over 200,000 years? On all sites associated with this species there is evidence indicating that stone tool manufacture was the norm. Examination of these stone implements gives the impression that Neanderthals were highly competent toolmakers, yet their tools varied little throughout the thousands of years the species was in existence, and often seem primitive in relation to those of *Homo sapiens*. Unlike *Homo sapiens*, Neanderthals did not design tools for specific purposes, and they never worked materials other than wood or stone.

Judging by their large brain size, Neanderthals could have been more or equally intelligent when compared with modern humans, so why did they only develop fairly primitive tools? Perhaps other things were more important to them, or their abilities lay in other directions. Or perhaps the answer is far simpler – maybe it's not only brain *size* but brain *structure* that matters.

The modern human brain is made up of approximately 100 billion brain cells (neurons), contained, on average, in a volume of 1370 cubic centimetres. Even if the volume is larger or smaller than this average, the number of neurons remains roughly the same. This implies that, while brain size and number of neurons are important, cell density and the connectivity between the cells are equally important. It may well be that Neanderthals had brains of the same volume, or even bigger, than ours (containing fewer, the same or more neurons), but the density and connectivity between those neurons must surely have been different.

Whatever the truth of the matter, Neanderthals clearly had a highly developed intelligence; without it they could never have survived. They showed amazing knowledge when it came to stone tool manufacture, and great thought and perception in understanding their environment and the resources in it. However, it would appear to be a very different intelligence from that possessed by *Homo sapiens*. Significantly, about 50,000 years ago, despite their intelligence, the Neanderthals died out.

The comparison of Neanderthal man with *Homo sapiens* is vitally important in our quest for intelligence. We need to bear in mind the importance of brain size and structure when we look at insects and machines. And we also need to ask whether intelligence in certain areas is more important than intelligence in others. Did *Homo sapiens*, with a superior form of intelligence, cause the extinction of the less developed Neanderthal? Unfortunately, many of these questions are likely to remain unanswered, at least as far as Neanderthals are concerned.

OTHER EVOLUTIONARY FACTORS

Throughout an evolution such as ours, many changes – both physical and mental – occur. Although factors such as changing environment may influence these mutations, they themselves work as a feedback system. This means that one alteration affects something else, which in turn may affect something else, which can itself further affect the original alteration, and so on. For instance, by moving into, or altering its environment, a species can, possibly unwittingly, bring about an evolutionary change in itself. Once in a particular environmental setting, a species may evolve so as to be better suited to that environment. With this in mind, what important factors may have influenced the phenomenal increase in human brain size during our evolution?

Brains are, in terms of energy, highly expensive. Their regular energy requirement, in comparison with other parts of the human body, is tremendous. It has been estimated[4] that in the last million years the increase in human brain size alone has necessitated a corresponding increase of 9 per cent in children's nutritional requirements. Furthermore, human brain metabolism accounts for as much as 22 per cent of our total body requirements, whereas in a chimpanzee it is only 8 per cent. A rapid growth in brain size would therefore have required an equally rapid increase in energy intake.

Along with their changing brain size, hominids began to change their diet – eating meat, rather than plants, as it provided a good source of energy and protein. This change in diet also went hand in hand with a change in site location. Fossil evidence shows that the hominids began to occupy more open areas, on the plains of Eastern Africa, where seasonal changes forced a greater reliance on meat because of the unavailability of regular plant supplies. Meat-eating had its own repercussions. It required less gut tissue than that needed to digest a solely vegetarian diet. The gut is another area of the body which has relatively high energy requirements, so its shortening freed up further energy which could also be used by the brain.

As the hominid diet and metabolism changed, so too did the way in which this diet was obtained and prepared. Considerable social changes had to take place, requiring the need for more systematic group organisation and structure.

All this was only possible because of a critically important event which had occurred much earlier in our existence. Around 6.5 million years ago we began to move on two legs.

The reasons why we adopted bipedalism are not clear. Proposed explanations have ranged from a change in our environment or diet, to the effects of the new social structures. The most popular theory[5] points to the need for a more efficient means of travel due to a thinly spread dispersion of the diet. I, myself, am not convinced by this theory. Evidence from the present-day animal world shows that standing on two legs is more commonly used for defence, for greater vision, or to enable greater and more flexible movement (reaching for things, etc). In the case of birds, the evolution of the upper limbs for other purposes, namely flying, resulted in the two lower limbs remaining on the ground. Using our upper limbs for other purposes, possibly coupled with a better early warning system, would seem to offer far more convincing reasons for bipedalism.

Like all evolutionary adaptations, bipedalism has had its own knock-on effects. As our ancient ancestors rose to their feet their eyes moved to the front of their heads, making sight by far the most important sense. This emphasis on vision is found throughout the primate world and is associated with a larger brain size. As the eyes are positioned at the front of the head, stereoscopic vision is produced. In present-day *Homo sapiens* approximately 70 per cent of brain operation is concerned with vision.[6] So the importance of this aspect of brain development cannot be stressed too highly.

A further, possibly even more important, result of bipedalism was that the larynx was freed for development, thus giving hominids the apparatus which would eventually allow them to speak. Language has been regarded for many years as one of the most important aspects of humanity. Without evolving bipedal locomotion we would never have been able to communicate in the way we do today.

Nowadays we consider a number of specific characteristics to be indicative of intelligence. These include art, music, spatial awareness, mathematical ability, language and even physical adeptness, but how did these features develop? It is worth attempting to identify a point in our history when characteristics such as these first appeared.

THE PALAEOLITHIC REVOLUTION

Although *Homo sapiens* came into existence around 100,000 years ago, they did not bring with them an entirely new material culture. This was not to occur until the middle/upper Palaeolithic transition – that is, 60,000 to 30,000 years ago. It was then that a cultural explosion occurred. In this relatively short space of time more innovations took place than had occurred in the preceding *six million years* of evolution.

Many separate changes characterised this cultural revolution. For the first time art was used as a form of expression, both in painting (on cave walls) and as personal decoration (body tattooing and jewellery – teeth and bone pendants and beads). New methods of tool production were used, bringing with them an increase in tool numbers and a broadening of their uses. Settlements became more permanent and people began to live less nomadic lifestyles, providing a greater opportunity for trade. Hunting techniques and weapons changed as the need for greater amounts of food grew with the population, and the habitation of areas previously considered inhospitable became more common.

The middle/upper Palaeolithic transition was, then, clearly a period of massive change, but why? We know that it was not simply a matter of our own 'vastly more intelligent' species arriving on the scene, bringing with it a whole range of new artefacts. The answer is far more complicated. The new artefacts and underlying changes in thought processes were associated with the same species who, for thousands of years prior to the transition, had existed with primitive tools and culture – *Homo sapiens*. So what was it that caused these relatively quick changes within the minds of early humans?

Answering this question would take us towards solving the puzzle of intelligence, its origins and components. Unfortunately, however, there is no easy solution. The different suggested theories include many different causes, from the re-structuring of social relations to the development of language to the appearance of economic specialisation or even a technological 'invention' similar to that which caused the transition to agriculture 30,000 years later.

SOCIETY AND INTELLIGENCE

One thing is certain: the pace of change, which hotted up 50,000 years ago, has continued to hot up ever since and is continuing to do so now. If a creature's lifestyle is changing little then the intelligence needed to follow that lifestyle needs to change little. If, however, a species' lifestyle changes rapidly then the intelligence of that species needs to change rapidly too. This is likely to mean that intelligence will get stronger and more powerful in ways which are relevant to that species' development. By the same token, intelligence may stagnate or even weaken in aspects of life that become less important to that species.

As we have seen, intelligence is both multi-faceted and subjective. This subjectivity is reflected in terms of society and culture. Each person's intelligence is directly linked to the environment in which they exist. It is therefore useful to look back at past civilisations in order to see how ancient peoples survived and succeeded, and what was and was not important to them.

As we look at our development as a species, we can see that

changes in our technology, hunting techniques, food procurement and storage have led to massive social change. We have gone from small nomadic bands of hunter gatherers, to small agricultural villages, to towns, to huge cities. How have these changes affected the way people think, and display their intelligence?

The way a society is structured says a lot about how the individuals within it think. However, a culture runs itself, everyone within it must conform, be looked after, know their place and feel part of it. Out of the hundreds of societies which have been in existence before our own, I have selected a few which give some interesting clues to the relationship between social structure and intelligence.

Social Structure

Within traditional American Indian society there was no class system. Instead the centre of life was the family. Society was usually matriarchal: often the women decided who would become tribal leader, removing them if they were dissatisfied.[7]

In contrast, Ancient Greek society was state-run, and possessed several classes of people: citizens, women, those of non-citizen parentage, slaves and foreigners. Those who were not citizens (including women) had no political say, had difficulty getting an education and were regarded as socially and intellectually inferior in all respects to those who were citizens.

As in some of the Indian tribes, for the Greeks the concept of the family was different from our own. In Ancient Greece the term *oikois* was used to refer to the household. Each *oikois* contained not only family members, but also slaves and friends. The male head of the household had under his protection women, slaves and any of his sons who were still at home. In Greek society women were not regarded as independent beings, and were seen as physically, morally, socially and intellectually inferior to men. In fact, among the rich, even sex with a woman was seen as being more for the sake of procreation, while sex with males was for pleasure.

Like the Ancient Greeks, the Romans had a class-based society. People fitted into one of a number of groups: citizens, freedmen, foreigners or slaves. Citizenship was gained through birth, through a decree from the emperor, or because Rome's boundaries had expanded to encompass your home. Slaves had no rights whatsoever; children born to slaves automatically became slaves themselves. As with the Greeks, slaves were considered to have low intelligence, particularly in comparison to their masters.

Due to the extent of slave labour, all classes, apart from the slaves themselves, were able to enjoy vast amounts of leisure time. Any necessary work was usually completed in the morning, leaving the afternoon and evening free for more relaxing occupations. Much of this leisure time was spent at the theatre watching plays, or at the stadium watching chariot races and other sports. Unlike the Greeks the Romans preferred to watch sport rather than take part in it themselves. Tourism was another popular activity, including trips to such places as Egypt. Music and dance were not as important to Roman society – Cicero once commented, 'no one who is sober dances unless he happens to be mad'.[8]

Clearly, in the 3000 years since Greek civilisation existed, and 2000 years since the Romans, there have been many changes. In contrast to Greek society, in Roman society the intelligence of women and men was considered to be more equal. In the Western world today women and men are considered to have equal rights and intelligence but this is not accepted in other parts of the world.

Education

Education is another aspect of life that is closely bound up with intelligence. Again, a brief look at ancient educational systems may help to shed some light on the ways different societies have nurtured and measured intelligence.

In American Indian societies formal education was very different from our own, being more practical in its approach, and beginning at the age of three or four.[9] Boys were subjected to numerous 'toughening-up' exercises, such as being plunged into icy water, stung with ants or left in the scorching sun with a mouthful of water which they were not allowed to swallow.[10] They were also taught more practical survival techniques such as fishing and how to hunt with model weapons.

Girls, however, followed their mothers, learning how to carry out domestic work and look after younger siblings. Both girls and boys were told how to collect such things as fruit, nuts and berries.

Within Aztec life the teaching of the children took two forms: that undertaken by parents and that which took place in school. Training by parents included the teaching of crafts such as pottery and basket-making. For commoners basic morals and religious education were taught, along with ritual dancing, singing and rhetoric. Boys received military training and girls received religious instruction. Amongst the nobility, schoolchildren were trained for leadership, whether in political, military or religious life. An 'assisted places scheme' existed, which allowed the most intelligent of the commoners (those who performed best at school) to also receive a 'noble' education.

Education in Ancient Greece varied according to gender. For girls it was limited to learning about manual or domestic tasks. For boys, however, education was far more challenging. At the age of seven they would begin to study subjects such as basic literacy, music and physical education with the occasional inclusion of mathematics. The development of a Greek alphabet meant that, to take part fully in society and politics, boys had to learn to read and write.

The Roman education system was based on that of the Greeks. Up to the age of twelve, reading, writing and arithmetic were taught using both Greek and Latin. Children used a wax tablet to write on and had abacuses for mathematics, while the Latin alphabet helped to teach the sounds of letters. For girls, education was not considered that important. Most girls therefore learnt only the basics. Some daughters of senators did, however, receive a good education. At middle school, literature, advanced arithmetic and rhetoric were taught. The ability to speak well in public was very important and, by and large, dictated the success an individual could achieve in public life. To this end, further studies included oratory and philosophy.

In modern societies the ability to read and write is extremely important. Even the poorest cultures in the world strive to learn basic literacy, although, as we saw from ancient schooling systems, this does not seem to have been given that much importance in the past. While most societies had a form of written language, it was only the richest and most fortunate who had the opportunity to learn it. How important was the ability to write, then, in the cultures we are looking at?

American Indians were very unusual in that, even up until modern times, their languages were never written down. The one exception to this is the language of the Cherokee, which was first put into written form in the 1820s. Stories of Indian life were simply passed from generation to generation verbally.

The Inca world did not possess a written form of communication either. Instead they used a complicated system of strings tied into long fringes, known as *quipu*. These *quipus* used knotting, colour and position to indicate meaning, and vast amounts of records kept in this way have been discovered. Unfortunately the system is so far beyond anything we understand today that much of its meaning has been lost.

Other societies did not use a true written language; instead pictures and symbols indicated meaning. Examples of such 'writing' come from both the Aztecs and from the hieroglyphics of Ancient Egypt. Hieroglyphics were used as inscriptions on tombs and monuments, with hieratic script (a code form of even simpler pictures) being used for records, literature and religious texts. The Greek and Roman worlds, however, placed far more importance on the ability to read and write. Both societies had alphabets, and fully scripted languages, and taught reading and writing at school.

Architecture

In today's world the majority of individuals live together in towns or cities. Modern cities are vast, with buildings reaching high into the sky. We may consider ourselves far better than any past culture because of this ability to build, but there is evidence that the cities of the past were also great.

The Aztecs populated the region now known as Mexico. At its peak the Aztec capital housed something like 250,000 people, making it four times as large as Henry VII's London of the time.[11] The Spaniards referred to Mexico as 'another Venice' because of its streets of canals, laid out on a grid pattern which the modern city still adheres to. An aqueduct brought in fresh water from the mountains to supply this vast city which contained schools, houses, shops and public lavatories. One of the most interesting features was the Emperor's zoological gardens, which had no parallel in Europe. They contained a large aviary which housed all kinds of birds including the Royal Eagle, pools for flamingoes, as well as enclosures for big cats, wolves, snakes and small carnivores. (It was said that the Aztecs, a warring civilisation, fed the bodies of their enemies to the carnivore section of their zoo.)[12]

Aztec cities, unlike European cities of the time, were very clean, with barges taking away waste which was recycled as fertiliser. This environmental cleanliness was matched by that of the people. They bathed daily, and considered the Spaniards, who bathed very rarely, to be smelly and disgusting.

The Inca Empire was truly immense. It covered Peru, Bolivia, Ecuador, most of Chile and a large area of Argentina, and was made up of a number of colonial cities, each mimicking the style of the vast capital. A total of 22,500 kilometres of paved roads connected these cities, the remains of which can still be seen today.[13]

The structures most famed from Egyptian times are, of course, the pyramids. These pyramids were immense creations, made from huge stone blocks. Although the wheel was available, the blocks, each weighing around 2 tonnes, were probably drawn on sledges hauled over log paths, covered in mud for lubrication. The average pyramid needed over two million blocks, each requiring highly accurate placement. For instance, the base of the Great Pyramid of Cheops extends over a flat area of 53,077 square metres with a maximum margin of error of 21mm.[14] The faces of the limestone and granite blocks were cut so cleanly, before being fitted together, that a thin blade still cannot be slotted between them.

The blocks used for constructing pyramids have often been found to have markings on them. These have been translated as inscriptions such as 'Khephoen is great' (ancient grafitti) or as instructions for construction workers such as 'this side up' and 'for the outer world'.[15] As it took several thousand men anything between ten and thirty years to actually construct a pyramid, it was important that such instructions were given; the surveyors and overseeing scribes who commenced the project were often not the ones who completed it. Here we can see a clear link between intelligence, language, literacy and the completion of large-scale building projects.

IDENTIFYING THE MARKS OF INTELLIGENCE

In this chapter we have taken a brief look at human evolution and a few early civilisations in our search for the beginnings of intelligence. A number of points showed themselves to be important: brain size, bipedalism, changes in diet and tool development, for instance, have all played their part. But none of them can be said to be the sole answer – the trigger for intelligent behaviour as we know it.

We have seen time and again how one evolutionary change sparks off many others, but the problem is that we have no way of knowing what came first. For example, was it eating meat that caused brains to increase in size? Or was it the increase in brain size that triggered the need for greater nutrients and thus led to meat-eating? We can guess, judging from the archaeological record, that intelligence, as we know it, did not occur until much later in our development, but we cannot say *when*.

Around 40,000 years ago evidence for a fully rounded culture did start to appear – for example art, musical instruments and jewellery. All these items are, not surprisingly, associated with our own species. But modern humans have existed for at least the last 100,000 years. Why then did such cultural artefacts take so long to appear?

When looking at the civilisations of the past we have seen how, in each case, the expression of intellect in an individual was directly linked to the social and cultural values of each civilisation at that particular time. For the Romans public speaking was a key indicator, whereas for the Greeks music and physical agility were important. For American Indians and the Aztecs, bravery and prowess in battle were the most highly prized qualities. Just as we might now regard a person's ability to operate a computer as a sign of intelligence, so presumably would the Incas have regarded the ability to understand and use *quipu*.

According to popular myth, one of the first human inventions was the wheel. Yet this could not be further from the truth. American Indians did not develop it; and, due to their fine canal networks, Aztecs and Incas had no use for it, other than in toys. Despite this they were very successful societies. We must be careful therefore about how closely we link creativity and invention with intelligence, particularly with regard to artefacts peculiar to one society. Certain cultures regard the invention of the wheel as an intelligent act but this is a subjective view – the importance attributed to the wheel depends on the value placed on it by the observer's own culture.

THE FUTURE OF INTELLIGENCE

As societies have evolved, it seems that the intelligence required to succeed within them has also evolved. The ability to interact with technology, for example, has now become vital for success on a global scale. Where will this take us in the future? Our intelligence will probably evolve, but how quickly? While the intelligence of a typical Aztec, Greek or Roman was sufficient to cope with the world around them, can the same be said of people today?

As a species, we humans are designed to live off the land; and we have engineered our way of life to reap the maximum rewards from the earth. In the last century however, we have, in many ways, created an artificial environment for ourselves, devoid of many aspects of the real world. What form of intelligence is best suited to this relatively new environment? Certainly it must be different from that which helped us survive harsh physical conditions of the past. We need to ask ourselves whether our intelligence can meet the challenge of the massive advancements our future must surely hold.

Amongst the many factors involved in the evolution of human

intelligence, none has caused as much controversy as language. Language has long been considered to be one of the most intelligent features of human behaviour, a feature not believed to be displayed by any other species, but perhaps this is untrue. Maybe other creatures can be taught to communicate with one another. When did language appear and in what form? Why is it considered so important? These and other vital questions are explored in the next chapter.

3

LANGUAGE AND INTELLIGENCE

H UMANS COMMUNICATE IN A WAY which many consider to be unique, through the use of fully symbolic vocalisations (noises which represent things). Producing a symbol (not only those used in language, but also those in art and music) involves planning and executing a mental concept. This concept relates to some object, event or previously used symbol and may have an emotional meaning attached to it. Common symbols require links to be made across different mental domains; thus the symbols form a common basis for description.

To be able to symbolise efficiently requires specific mental processes. In humans this ability is learned while still very young. A typical child utters their first coherent words around eighteen months of age.[1] By the age of two the word count is generally around fifty and the child is beginning to attach meaning to them. Often, however, some of the words may be pronounced incorrectly. I can remember my own daughter, Maddi, referring to 'munk' as opposed to the correct 'milk'.

From two or three years of age a child increases their vocabulary at an amazing rate. They begin to form sentences, give orders and commands, and by the end of the period vocalise over 1000 words. By the age of six their vocabulary has extended to something like 13,000 words, while by the age of eighteen it is typically 60,000 words.[2] This means that between the ages of two and eighteen a child learns, on average, over ten words a day, words which they can remember and make fluent use of. At its peak a child's learning rate is approximately one word per hour, every waking hour. These statistics are well worth remembering for any adult attempting to learn a foreign language.

So a child has to learn tens of thousands of words, but it does not end there. These words have to be fitted into a complex grammatical framework. If this does not occur, little sense will be made of what is said. In all languages it is not only the correct words which need to be uttered in order to convey meaning, they also have to be placed correctly within a sentence, and the sentence within a paragraph, and so on.

THE ORIGINS OF LANGUAGE

In his book *The Language Instinct* Steven Pinker (Professor of Brain and Cognitive Sciences at MIT) suggested that 'language is not a cultural artefact'. This is, I feel, blatant rubbish. We are not born with language. Indeed, even if we are born in one country to parents of another culture, we learn the language that is spoken around us, whatever that might be. What we do appear to have, however, is a genetic (programed) drive to learn to communicate through language. There are approximately 6000 languages in use throughout the modern world.[3] How did they arise and develop?

A strong case has been made for the theory that language developed as a hunting aid, which later spread into wider society.[4] Simple messages could be passed to provide geographical information, explain strategy and to co-ordinate plans to catch prey. The greater the complexity of such messages, the more information is being passed, resulting, one would expect, in a correspondingly higher success rate.

Many species have evolved to use vocal distress signals, uttered when predators are nearby. Other group members recognise these signals and run to safety when they are heard. Human language could have begun in a similar way, starting with the basic 'run for it' signal and developing to include more detailed information, such as, identifying the type of predator, and predicting where it is heading. This could be further modified for discussion on hunting techniques, later passing into everyday use.

The most important function of language is that it allows us to pass on and exchange information with others. This need not be done vocally; gestures and hand signals can sometimes be used instead. Anyone who has played the party game charades will, though, have experienced the problems associated with the expression of abstract concepts using only movement of body parts.

Those unable to vocalise, for one reason or another, do, however, use a recognised language of hand signs, and it has been suggested that our verbal language evolved from a similar type of gestural language. While using gestures and signals does, of course, make it much more difficult to communicate in the dark, it provides a far more accurate and powerful means of communicating over a distance in silence. For early humans, then, gesturing would have been a mixed blessing. While substantially improving the fortunes of a hunt, it would have severely hampered social communication.

It is amazing just how many different theories exist to explain how human language originated and developed. The real answer is, however, non-provable and because of this the subject is rife with speculation and conjecture. Some say[5] that in the early stages language was messy, with few rules, and that natural sounds such as hoots and grunts probably appeared first. There is a fair amount of logic in this. Look at other species of bird, fish and mammals – they all perform rudimentary communication and signalling through the use of both sound and visual stimuli. It is therefore likely that human language initially took the form of noises and visual gestures.

One of the more unusual theories goes as far as suggesting that human language could have evolved from, and is therefore closely linked to, music and song. The main problem with this idea is that musical skills are present in the right hemisphere of the brain, while those of language are on the extreme left. Although words and music appear to fit snugly together, as far as the brain is concerned they appear to be distinctly different yet complementary skills.[6] In fact many of the most famous songwriters have been a duo, involving one person composing the tune and the other providing the words. This makes it extremely difficult to agree with the concept of human language originating from music.

STRENGTH IN NUMBERS

It has been proposed by Robin Dunbar, Professor of Psychology at the University of Liverpool, that the reason speech developed was in order to maintain social contacts – language as a medium for gossip. We all spend a vast majority of our time talking, but how often do we actually impart relevant information? Gossiping and chatting to friends is something we do every day. In fact in human conversation 60 per cent of the time is taken up with gossip, but why?

While some species use a few simple rules with which to conduct their social lives, monkeys, apes and humans require sophisticated knowledge about each other. Why is this?

Social complexity has been found to increase exponentially according to the number of members in a group. This makes sense. Consider a group of four individuals: while there are three relationships between myself and the other members, there are only three further separate relationships between the other members. Now look at a group consisting of eight members: while I have seven links with the others, there are twenty-one separate other relationships going on.

When the number of members reaches 100, my links total ninety-nine, while there are a further 4841 other separate links in existence. So, although my own immediate links relate directly to group size, far more detached links (which I potentially need to understand) also exist. It is clear that the greater the number of individuals in a group, the more intelligent each individual must be in order to keep track of who is friends with who.

For each species of primate the optimum group size is different. Is there a way in which we can discover how big a group can be? Perhaps a closer look at the brain of a mammal could reveal the answer.[7]

An individual mammal's brain essentially consists of three regions: the primitive, inner brain, known as the cerebellum, for everyday survival including muscle co-ordination; the brain stem, containing the inner brain, which communicates sensory and motor signals; and finally the neocortex, or simply cortex, for initiating motor actions, understanding and possibly even emotions.

In a fish the cerebellum can take up to 90 per cent of the total volume of the brain. Conversely, for most mammals the neocortex takes up 30 to 40 per cent of the total brain volume. In primates, however, it makes up a much higher percentage, particularly in humans where it is about 80 per cent. As a consequence, the neocortex is felt to be the 'thinking' part of the brain.

Many researchers have attempted to link the physical character-istics of the brain in different primates to behaviours displayed by that species. And one of these studies has found a good correlation between the neocortex volume of a primate species and the mean size of a group in that species. The bigger the neocortex volume, the bigger the group size witnessed, and therefore the larger number of relationships an individual of that species can cope with.

The neocortex ratio (the ratio of neocortex volume to the volume of the remainder of the brain) arguably appears to provide the best fit with group size. In humans this ratio is about 4:1 (which corre-sponds to the 80 per cent figure given earlier). By looking at the neocortex ratio in all the (non-human) primates and relating this to mean group size in that species, a projected mean group size for humans can be estimated. This appears to be around 150 (or 147.8, to be precise).

At 150 a group of humans is so large that maintaining and estab-lishing friendships would require each individual to spend 42 per cent of their time on physical social grooming.[8] This would clearly be impossible, as it would leave insufficient time for hunting, foraging, eating, sleeping and many other vital activities. How, then, did our ancestors solve this problem? It has been suggested that language developed as an alternative to physical grooming. Imagine how many individuals could be 'groomed' verbally at any one time. Language may, then, have developed as a social tool: a way of enhancing and establishing close ties with other individuals; of generally helping to maintain social standing, as a medium of gossip.

THE POWER OF SPEECH

An important feature which had to appear before language could develop was the physical ability to make either sounds or gestures. When our ancestors became bipedal the larynx dropped in the body, much lower in fact than in any other primate including chimpanzees or gorillas. The part of the throat directly above the larynx, just behind the tongue, was therefore freed. It is this space which is necessary in order to utter sounds. In bipeds, such as humans, the spinal cord links with the brain vertically from below, rather than horizontally from behind. This means that the larynx can be closed off, so that humans can hold their breath, producing a less harsh sound.

All human languages use a finite number of sounds, producing an infinite number of complex meanings. The placement of the larynx allows consonants to be emitted which break up the continuous sound flow and allow for enhanced coding in vocal language. For words to be produced, however, all the physical capabilities must be present: that is, the ability to move the lips, tongue and jaw in a cohesive, concurrent way. It is these movements that are learnt and which differ greatly between different cultures.

Further investigations of the language area within the human brain have shown that it consists of two regions, termed Wernicke's area and Broca's area. Damage suffered to either of these areas results in the loss of some language skills; comprehension is affected with injury to Wernicke's area and grammar with Broca's area. If, however, the connections between the two areas are harmed all aspects of language suffer.

Casts taken from the fossilised skulls of our ancestors give us some insight into when these areas may have developed. While not present in the *Australopithecines*, a two-million-year-old early *Homo* species does show significant development in Broca's area.[9] This means that hominids from two million years ago probably had both the physical and mental developments in place to allow language to occur.

ANIMAL COMMUNICATION

Humans may, then, have been using language to communicate for two million years, but are we the only species to express ourselves to each other? Some of the most biased conclusions have been drawn, as far as other species and language are concerned. While it has been conceded that many other species may have rudimentary language, some purists still insist that only humans have the true means to communicate with each other. They feel that the bark of a dog, or squeal of a pig are only sounds uttered out of excitement or aggression.

Despite the doubters, studies have shown that many species have extremely rich vocabularies. For example, vervet monkeys call between each other to distinguish different predators. They use different calls to warn of leopards, eagles and snakes, while Gelada monkeys call to each other about the availability of different foods and use moans and grunts, during grooming, to hint at what they would like.

Perhaps most astoundingly, researchers have discovered that not only do different species communicate, but that different dialects can be found within a species. For example, crows in Central Europe caw differently to those in the West. The Czech description of a cock's call is a 'kikiriki', one syllable less than the English equivalent 'cock-a-doodle-doo'. Japanese macaques produce a 'coo' which is very different in the North than in the South. The calls and noises of different species can be very complex indeed, particularly when other factors such as visual stimuli and environmental input are taken into account. We, as humans, can only look in from the outside. It may therefore be impossible for us to ever know the true complexity and extent of communication in other species.

In spite of all the evidence for communication and even dialects within other species many linguists still tend to believe in the purity and wonder of the human language. In fact a set of eighteen key features have been identified to define 'true' language,[10] the main points being:

- learning
- syntax (structure)
- words do not resemble objects (e.g. 'chair' does not resemble a chair)
- reference (sounds relate to objects)

It is worth pointing out that all these characteristics inevitably derive from the starting point taken by such linguists: that human language is marvellous and everything about it is superior to communication amongst all other species. Important factors observed in the communication of other species are simply ignored because they are different from human communication and are therefore not considered important. Factors such as communication distance, robustness against errors, and speed are, in reality, also very important. But they all tend to be ignored. In our search for intelligence we must ensure that we do not fall into the same trap.

HUMAN–ANIMAL COMMUNICATION

Most animal owners dream of being able to converse properly with their pets, although any attempts to do this, apart from in Hollywood films, generally prove unsuccessful. Despite this, there have been many studies which have attempted to teach other creatures to communicate in a human way. In the 1950s the Hayes family undertook such a project, when they reared a baby chimp alongside their own child, attempting to treat both as equally as possible. Their hope was that, as the two grew up together, they would learn everything simultaneously: how to sit up, feed themselves, and of course talk. Sadly,

Vicki the Chimp could eventually utter no more than five or six words, and these only with great difficulty.

One of the conclusions drawn, from the Hayes experiment, and other similar escapades, was that chimps simply do not have the physical ability to speak in the same way as humans, their vocal systems being considerably different from our own. As a result, these types of experiments changed direction. Instead of trying to teach chimps to verbalise, an attempt was made to teach them sign language.

One of the first experiments was carried out by Alan and Trixie Gardner in the 1960s. They endeavoured to train a chimp, called Washoe, to use the American deaf and dumb sign language, ASL. Washoe was tutored every day and eventually learnt around 100 signs, each individual gesture indicating a word or concept. Eventually Washoe could carry out conversations with other signing humans. However, many critics of the project pointed out that Washoe's signed sentences were almost always, apart from repetitions, only two signs long.

The 1970s saw the start of numerous studies involving the teaching of sign language to orang-utans, gorillas and chimpanzees. The most notable was the work of psychologist David Premack who taught a chimp named Sarah to use different-coloured plastic shapes to stand for different concepts. Because Sarah put together such shapes on a board, in order to spell out sentences, Premack argued that she could understand abstract concepts such as 'same' or 'different'.[11]

The most long-term project in this field, is also, perhaps, the most important. It was begun in the 1970s by Duane and Sue Savage-Rumbaugh at the Yerkes Language Research Centre in the USA (named after Robert Yerkes, some of whose work we will discuss later). They developed a computer keyboard language named 'Yerkish', made up of coloured shapes. Their greatest triumph was a pigmy chimpanzee called Kanzi. Perhaps the most important aspect of Kanzi's ability to use the symbols was the fact that he began to pick up their meaning before formal training began. His mother was being trained in their use while he was merely a newborn and it seems he picked up the language almost like a human child – in the first months and years of his life.

By the age of six, Kanzi could recognise 150 symbols and under-stand sentences never previously encountered, when known symbols were strung together. Kanzi also took on some basic grammatical rules and even invented some of his own. This said, Kanzi's abilities do not rank with those of a typical three-year-old, as he is limited to two- or three-word sentences which relate solely to what he wants. While his communication is relatively slow and stuttering it appears that he certainly has the ability to relate abstract meanings to symbols. Although he is able to interpret some relatively complex human expressions, he cannot communicate with humans as freely or as deeply as perhaps Geladas or other chimps when calling to each other in the wild.

Chimpanzees have a brain structure which is similar to that of humans, although it is smaller and differently proportioned. We would then perhaps expect the results we see, that chimps do the best they can with human communication, but fall short of the abilities of a typical human child with its much larger brain. So is human language directly linked to brain size and structure?

ALEX THE PARROT

Another line of research is concerned with the ability of parrots to copy human speech, an ability regarded, by some, as mindless mimicry. However, studies have been undertaken to discover if they can understand human language as well as copy it.

The late 1970s saw the start of an extraordinary research pro-gram, run by Irene Pepperberg, at the University of Arizona. The principal subject was Alex, a 22-year-old African grey parrot. His training mainly involved two humans teaching each other about a subject while Alex watched. This approach closely linked with studies which have shown that children best learn difficult tasks by watching others and them trying for themselves. Alex watches one person ask the other person about an object e.g. 'what colour'. The respondent is then awarded or scolded for their answer, depending on whether they answered correctly or not. The roles of teacher and respondent are then reversed to show that words and behaviour are not unique to an individual, thus preventing Alex associating certain words and actions with particular individuals.

An important part of Alex's teaching is that when he, himself, answers a question correctly he is rewarded with an object which relates to the word he used. If, for example, he refers to a 'key', he receives a key; in order to receive a 'nutty' reward he must ask for it, by saying 'wanna nut'. This is in direct contrast with other research done in this field, where parrots have received edible treats whatever their answers. Pepperberg believes that her approach reinforces Alex's idea of what each object is, while offering a nut when the answer was 'key' merely serves to confuse and mislead the birds.

It has been found that Alex can count; he can also associate words with numbers and therefore understand a representation of quantity. In addition, he has learnt concepts such as 'same' and 'different' and can say which attributes are the same or different, e.g. colour or size. If there are no similarities between objects, he will say 'none'. He is able to respond directly to specific questions and achieves an accuracy score of about 80 per cent. Alex understands the names of fifty different objects and can quantify them in terms of colour, material and shape, combining these classifications where appropriate. For example, he can count the number of round, green items on a tray.

Many of Alex's skills are beyond the capabilities of any other non-human biological creature (including the 'cleverest' chimpanzees), and yet, parrots' brains are very different from those of

primates. The outer layer (cerebral cortex), which, it has been suggested, plays a major role in human intelligence, is in little evidence
in parrots. What, if anything, does this tell us? As Alex uses the brain
that he has, perhaps it weakens the link between possessing a cerebral
cortex and developing language, or, more fundamentally, the link
between language and intelligence.

The Characteristics of Human Communication

Humans communicate with other humans in a relatively complex way,
which is suited to our physical capabilities and our mental attributes.
We follow particular standardised methods of assigning names to both
real-world and abstract objects and follow set procedures in signalling
to each other. Around the earth rules differ, as do the names, and
sounds, used for objects. Some humans can readily learn to switch
from one set of symbols to another, whilst others, such as myself,
have great difficulty in doing so.

Inside a human brain our thoughts consist essentially of electrochemical signals, each thought being a state of the brain. We learn
to link such brain states with certain symbols for communication. For
example if I think of an 'ice-cream', I have learnt to associate that
thought with the word or spoken sound of 'ice-cream'. Human
language thus depends very much on how we interact with the world
and our senses, just as it relates to our mental framework.

If a person is deaf, dumb or blind, they are not necessarily any
less intelligent than any other person. They may have difficulty using
human language or communication skills because their physical
abilities are different, so their task is a much more difficult one. Other
species not only have physical differences but also, as in the case of
Alex the parrot, a completely different mental male-up. A human
being, or other creature, with absolutely no ability to interact with

the outside world is an extremely difficult case. How can their intelligence be assessed if no feedback can be obtained? We should not say that such an individual is not intelligent, but rather that we are unable to assess their intelligence. Surely the same must be true of all creatures other than humans. Even assessing a human in a language they cannot speak is almost impossible!

The ability to communicate is certainly an important feature of an individual's intelligence. The way humans communicate is appropriate to humans, and the same is true for other species. We must be clear, however, that human-to-human communication, while being relatively complex in comparison with that of other species, is simply a form of communication that is appropriate for humans.

Human language has considerable limitations. Firstly, we have a limited syntax (set of language rules) for any human language. Secondly human speech is uni-dimensional – a collection of utterances appearing one after the other. We produce speech serially, in one dimension, and listen to it in the same, relatively slow fashion. Visually, humans employ two dimensions and we can think and infer visually in three dimensions – but in speech we just use one dimension. Other restricting factors include our relatively slow speed of message passing and our inability to learn languages other than human ones.

HUMAN COMMUNICATION AND MACHINE COMMUNICATION

When we compare human communication with machine capabilities, the differences are immediately apparent. Machine communication can occur in many different ways, including radio, microwave, and infrared. Signals can be transmitted and received at the speed of light (such as laser signals) and can appear almost instantaneously on the other side of the world. Millions of complex signals can be sent and received, in parallel, on the same pair of wires, with little or no error. Humans have employed these capabilities to assist in human communication, microphones translating the pressure waves of human speech into electronic signals prior to transmission and receivers translating them back again at the point of reception.

We have, then, effectively been able to use technology to make up for our own relatively poor performance. While a pair of humans can pass a small amount of information between them, a pair of machines can pass millions of times that amount.

Interestingly *all* of the eighteen key features mentioned earlier as defining 'true' language, also apply to machine communication, whether in the form of digital or analog signalling. But, as machines can communicate much more rapidly in a more complex way, what does this mean when we compare their communication and language abilities with our own? Is language, particularly speech, really such a critical element of intelligence?

When a human utters a sentence, they are converting from an electrochemical concept in their brain, into a sequence of mechanical (air pressure) sounds. The person hearing the message then converts these sounds back again from mechanical to electrochemical. Human language is just an agreed set of sounds which facilitates this. If, in the future, humans begin to communicate by thought signals alone, and spoken language becomes obsolete, will that mean that they are less intelligent than present-day humans, because they do not have the same language abilities as us? I think not. On the contrary, such individuals would be able to communicate much more efficiently and effectively, in a way more akin to that of machines than of humans.

The human ability to learn a language involves the physical and mental capability to do so, and also an appropriate exposure, over time, to that language. However, the relative importance of each is clearly debatable. There are also other important factors involved in language development and intelligence. For example, how much is our intelligence due to our genes, and how much is it due to our experiences?

4

NATURE VERSUS NURTURE

A VERY IMPORTANT ISSUE to be considered when looking at intelligence is the question of how it originates in individuals. Two opposing views have traditionally been held, each emphasising the importance of either nature or nurture. The belief has been that intelligence is *either* inherited *or* that it develops due to the environment in which an individual is born and bred. According to the 'nature' camp, an individual is born with their intelligence already in place. According to supporters of the 'nurture' theory, they are born with a clean slate and it is life's experiences which form their intelligence.

If we look at the modern definition cited earlier ('Intelligence is the ability to reason and to profit by experience. An individual's level of intelligence is determined by a complex interaction between their heredity and environment.'), we can see that it names *both* heredity and environment as contributing factors.

In the past, the majority view was usually either one way or the other, never a compromise. More often than not, the favoured theories on the origins of intelligence have been motivated by the political climate of the time. For example, in the nineteenth century society was ordered strictly by class, the upper classes being considered more intelligent and the lower classes 'feeble-minded' or 'idiots'. It was felt that this situation had been brought about by the genetic nature of intelligence. Through this inherited facility, it was believed that each group had a certain level of intelligence which they could not change and it was this that kept the upper classes leading the lower.

Throughout history, the concept of intelligence has been viewed in many ways and even those most closely connected with its study have had distinctly different ideas as to its characteristics. For example Lewis Terman, Professor of Education at Stanford University (USA) in the 1900s and hailed as the inventor of the term 'Intelligence Quotient (IQ)', regarded intelligence as an 'all round' general mental power.

Meanwhile in 1904 another pioneer, Charles Spearman, an eminent statistician and Professor of Psychology at University College, London (arguably the most influential Chair in Psychology in the UK) put intelligence down to 'the ability to deduce relationships'. In the 1950s, John Vernon, Professor of Educational Psychology at the University of Calgary in Alberta, Canada, claimed that intelligence consisted 'of several elements such as biological and behaviourist'. And, more recently, Linda Gottfredson, Professor of Educational Studies at the University of Delaware, referred to intelligence as 'the ability to deal with complexity'.

All these opinions in fact complement each other and indicate a different view of intelligence, each one perhaps reflecting the relevant ideas of the time. Each definition can be supported or squarely criticised, particularly if comparisons are made between humans, other creatures and machines. In reality 'intelligence' is a highly flexible concept – its meaning relating to the cultural background of the definer. But how have these different views arisen? And why do we feel so strongly about intelligence?

PREVIOUS VIEWS ON THE NATURE OF INTELLIGENCE

In third-century BC Greece, intelligence was thought to be hereditary. Plato, a leading philosopher of the time, stated that a person's intellect was class-related, with the upper classes possessing the highest levels of intellect. To maintain this status quo, individuals should only reproduce with others of their own class. He used the analogy of different metals – the upper classes were analogous to gold, the middle classes to silver, and so on. Just as it was acceptable to melt gold with gold, but not with say bronze, so it was acceptable for individuals of the upper class to reproduce with one another but not with a member of a lower class.[1] In the population as a whole, average levels of intelligence were further maintained by the destruction of those thought to be of extremely low intelligence; to this end children were killed at birth or in the early years if they were seen to display characteristics of 'idiocy'.

A century later views had changed. Levels of intelligence were now thought to be a result of environmental exposure – a product of teaching and life experience. Aristotle claimed that intelligence was due to evolution among living things and was therefore present in all citizens. This idea sounds reassuringly egalitarian at first. However, it must be remembered that at this time not all individuals had the rank of citizen. Slaves, labourers and most foreigners were all excluded from citizenship and therefore from being intelligent.

By the time of Cicero, in the early first century BC, the nature theory again held sway. Roman emperors were deemed to have intelligence well above that of normal citizens and were treated as living deities. The word 'intelligence' originated at this time, from *inthus lego* (loosely meaning 'to read mentally or understand').[1]

During the Middle Ages the concept of intelligence was again leaning towards the nature theory, and again there was a strict class system in force. Links were increasingly being made between intelligence and performance in particular taught subjects, such as music, grammar and psalms, because there was a shift toward the schooling of certain individuals. However this was not a widespread phenomenon; those lucky enough to be taught were usually those with money, and therefore those in the upper classes.

By the 1800s views on intelligence in the Western world were becoming far more open to debate, with both sides of the nature versus nurture argument represented. People like the philosopher and economist John Stuart Mill, who supported the nurture hypothesis, were, however, generally outnumbered by supporters of the nature side whose ideas reflected the capitalism and colonialism of that time.

One of those supporting nature was Herbert Spencer, a British social philosopher. In 1855 he wrote *Principles of Psychology*, in which he stated that intelligence was biologically rooted, and that internal order was related to external order. In other words intelligence was transmitted from parents to offspring, to the extent that mental peculiarities produced by habit gradually became hereditary over a number of generations (the inheritance of acquired characteristics). Clearly, evolutionary ideas were already in the air before Darwin's *Origin of Species by Means of Natural Selection* first appeared in 1859. In fact, contrary to popular belief, it appears to have been Spencer who coined the phrase 'survival of the fittest' and not Darwin.[2]

The publication of Darwin's work, along with that of other evolutionists, led to huge support for the hereditary nature of intelligence. This theory was used to bolster the idea of differences in intelligence between nations, races, classes and individuals, and this was in turn used to justify slavery and oppression. Further conclusions drawn from these works were that poorer sections of the population should be allowed to die out so that society could maintain a high level of intelligence. To this end poor people were not given social welfare, and in some parts of the world were not even allowed to breed.

THE TWO-FACTOR THEORY

The view that humans have an inherited level of intelligence was subscribed by Charles Spearman. He wanted to establish a scientific basis for the study of psychology and in particular the subject of intelligence. It was Spearman who, in 1904, invented factor analysis which is, essentially, a way of examining the statistical relationship of various numerical results. It works by taking a correlation between two measures (which is the degree they vary together from the average).

Spearman undertook a number of studies, in which he applied his theories, and the results were published in his paper 'General Intelligence: Objectively Determined and Measured'. These tests were done on schoolboys from a village school in Berkshire and from a preparatory school in Harrow. The measurements he took were firstly based on the teacher's assessment and ranking of the boys, then on the ranking of each by two of their schoolmates, and finally on each boy's ranking of himself, from a number of tests assessing his ability to discriminate weight, pitch and light. The results showed the correlation between intelligence and sensory measures, once they were adjusted, to be about 1.0 (1.0 being the highest correlation possible). The raw figures were actually 0.55, but Spearman devised a factor called 'attenuation' in order to arrive at the 'true' figure of 1.0. The second study he carried out on the boys looked at their examination grades in the subjects of Classics, French, English and Mathematics; he correlated them with the teachers ranking of the boys' musical ability. Again, after adjustment, this correlation was said to be 1.0.

After careful examination of the results Spearman concluded that there was an underlying factor present in the make-up of every individual which he termed 'general intelligence' or 'g'. He ended his paper by saying: 'We reach the profoundly important conclusion that there really exists a something that we may provisionally term "General Sensory Discrimination" and similarly a "General Intelligence" and further that the functional correspondence between these two is not appreciably less than absolute.'[3]

This 'g' factor was said to be genetically inherited and used in varying degrees during every act which involved intelligent thought; it was felt to be like an energy or power serving the whole nervous system. Spearman, however, saw that this underlying factor could not contain all the information which would be required mentally to do a specific activity. He believed that there was an additional factor at play, which he termed the 's' factor. This he defined as the knowledge possessed by an individual which was specific to a particular task that was being carried out.[4]

This type of analysis was termed 'the Two-Factor Theory' and it still survives, despite the fact that many more recent attempts to repeat Spearman's studies have not provided such conclusive results. Although positive correlations have been shown to exist they tend to be a lot lower than those found in Spearman's original study.

Taken together, the work of Spencer and Spearman actually provides substantial support for what is essentially a fairly straightforward approach to the complex subject of intelligence: an individual's intelligence depends on their brain. The brain is something that a human inherits, genetically, with its particular structure, size and content. This is the crux of the nature argument: if a person inherits their brain structure they must inherit their intelligence (or brain contents).

Throughout an individual's life, however, experiences cause some connections within the brain to get stronger through repeated use, and some to get weaker. This is due to signal strengths and synaptic weightings – the strengths of connections (synapses) within the brain. If a person is questioned on something in which he has had plenty of experience, due to a strong connection within the brain, the answers will come quickly and easily. Whereas a person questioned on something in which he has had little or no experience, would have made no previous connection, and would therefore answer slowly and less knowledgeably.

Perhaps 'g' should not be regarded as a single inherited entity, but rather as the complex physical make-up of an individual's brain *and* its connections with the outside world. Special factors can then be ascribed to the way an individual's brain has learnt to cope with a specific task. I believe that nature *and* nurture, rather than nature versus nurture, should be credited with the composition of intelligence.

INTELLIGENCE A AND INTELLIGENCE B

In 1949 O.D. Hebb, an American psychologist, made the first real attempt to draw a line under the nature versus nurture debate, in his paper 'The Organisation of Behaviour'. From studies he had carried out on individuals, both babies and adults, who had suffered some form of brain injury, he had concluded that there were, in fact, two different components present in intelligence. He observed that adult patients who underwent brain operations frequently showed little or no change in performance when sitting IQ tests before and after the operation. However, babies who underwent similar operations were more than likely to perform worse in such tests afterwards. He therefore claimed that one of the components of intelligence was diminished immediately when damage to the brain occurred and was a hereditary factor, while the other component remained relatively unaffected and was connected to experience. The hereditary factor was the capacity for 'elaborating perceptions and conceptual activities', while the experiential factor was 'the degree to which such elaboration has occurred'.[5]

The word 'intelligence' was felt by Hebb to have two meanings, which he termed Intelligence A and Intelligence B. Intelligence A was 'an Innate Potential, the capacity for development, a fully innate property that amounts to the possession of a good brain and good neural metabolism.' Intelligence B was defined as, 'the functioning of a brain in which developing has gone on, determining an average level of performance or comprehension by the partly grown or mature person.'[6] He stated that neither A, nor B, were directly observable, but that B was a 'Hypothetical level of development in brain function', and it was this which was measured in intelligence tests, whereas A was the 'original potential'.

If Hebb was correct then the nature versus nurture argument becomes redundant, as neither nature nor nurture are the controlling factors; it is a combination of both. In fact Hebb stated, on this very subject: 'The dispute in current literature has arisen, I believe, partly because of the double reference of the term "Intelligence" and partly because it has not been realised that if the effects of early experience are more or less generalised and permanent one can concede a major effect of experience on the IQ, and still leave the IQ its constancy and validity as an index of future performance.'[7]

FACTORS THAT INFLUENCE INTELLIGENCE

The Hebb view is really a form of the modern idea that Intelligence is affected to some degree by both nature and nurture, which is the most commonsense approach. Even this view, however, does not take into account the physical body in which the 'intelligence' is present.

In modern times looking at the physical container for intelligence has become very important because there is no longer only human intelligence to consider; we must also think about intelligence in animals and machines. As the Hebb definition ignores physical properties, it is rather like looking at the intelligence of a machine as being its main processing unit alone, with no connections in order to input or receive signals. But, without these physical commodities, allowing it to interact with the outside world, a machine, or indeed a human being, loses their intellectual effectiveness.

Nowadays research is no longer concerned with whether intelligence is a commodity produced simply by hereditary or environmental factors. Instead it attempts to discover to what degree it is affected by one or the other. In order to do this, both genetics and environmental situations have to be examined – which is not the easiest thing to do. For example, if a child from a poor background does not develop in terms of their intelligence as well as a child from a wealthy background, what is the reason? Is it because the poor child has not grown up in such a pleasant, stimulating environment? Is it because their genetic make-up is different? Or is it due to a mixture of the two?

Recent studies on factors that affect intelligence have not only taken into account the environment an individual is born into, but also the environment before birth. A report in *Nature* (1997), claimed that foetal development in the womb accounted for 20 per cent of an individual's total intelligence, and genetic influence was as little as 34 per cent. This idea does have some credibility as it is in this period of development that many neuron weightings and connections are arranged. It has also been observed that as early as three to four weeks after conception neuronal connections are being made and it may therefore be possible for babies, even at this stage, to feel pain.[8]

Linked with this research is the commercial goal to cash in on the human desire to have a more intelligent baby. It is now possible to buy a product called the 'Baby Plus' which has been marketed under the slogan 'Want a brainier baby?'. It is a walkman-type box which an expectant mother straps to her waist for the last sixteen weeks of pregnancy. The box plays sounds that mimic the mother's heartbeat. It is meant to stimulate the baby's brain, arouse curiosity and help brain cell development. Unfortunately it will be many years before we can measure how much truth there is in the manufacturer's claims.

The idea that genetic inheritance only accounts for 34 per cent of overall intelligence differs from the present, widely accepted, ratio which is generally put at a 60/40 split of inheritance/environment. These figures are, however, still subject to debate. For example, John C. Loehlin, Professor of Psychology and Computer Science at the University of Texas at Austin, USA, has done a great deal of research on genetic and environmental contributions in human personality traits and abilities. In a study of 850 twins, in 1976, he put the percentages as being close to 80/20 in favour of inheritance over environment. Such figures imply that there is not a great deal we can do to change the intelligence we are born with. And this idea has immediate knock on effects when it comes to issues such as race or class.

My own feeling is that applying percentages to intelligence, in this way, is just plain silly. It is like trying to say how much of an athlete's performance is due to the physical body they start with and how much is due to training. Perhaps we should rather liken intelligence to baking a cake. Nature would then be like the cake's ingredients, and nurture would be akin to the mixing and baking. The ingredients and making are, however, entirely different things. We do not say 60 per cent of a cake is due to the ingredients and 40 per cent to how it was made.

Using this analogy, we can take exactly the same ingredients and employ exactly the same method to make any number of cakes. Yet, even then, each cake will turn out to be slightly different from the last, making it impossible to estimate relative percentages of effect (ingredients versus mixing). This being the case, what chance do we stand when it comes to intelligence in individuals, where we do not know much about the 'ingredients' and it is virtually impossible to follow identical 'mixing' (educational) regimes for every individual?

Nevertheless the nature versus nurture argument rages on. Even in today's world, where scientific breakthroughs occur almost every week, political agendas still influence the theories of intelligence that are put forward. Nowadays we have a 'political correctness', which is used to prevent discrimination of any kind from being publicly displayed. This has affected the study of human intelligence in much the same way as the colonialism of the nineteenth century did. Then it was the accepted view that there were racial differences in intelligence due to inheritance and hence any research work reiterated this. Now it is widely felt that any racial differences are due to the inferior economic conditions under which most minority groups live, and thus environmental factors hold sway.

TWIN STUDIES

Will it ever be possible to bring the nature versus nurture argument to a satisfactory close? Given the right circumstances for a particular study the answer may well be yes. It has long been thought that the answer may lie in the investigation of identical twins. The ideal requirements for this study are that the twins have to have been separated at birth, and to have subsequently been brought up in families of different backgrounds, with no further contact with each other. If all of these criteria can be met, and the twins then discovered, then it is thought that a comparison of intelligence test results should provide the answer. If the results found prove to be remarkably similar it would show conclusively that intelligence is genetically inherited, whereas, if the results are seen to be substantially different, with the twin of the lower social status having a lower IQ, it would prove that the acquisition of intelligence depends on environmental factors.

However, such twins are very rare, and although various results have been obtained they have thus far been inconclusive. One of the main reasons for their rarity is that when twins are put up for adoption a great effort is made to keep them together. Where this is not possible they are generally placed in neighbouring families, of similar background, where they can remain in contact. Conversely, where twins have been separated at birth and adopted by different families, with different names, a long way apart, it is extremely unlikely that they will ever find out that they are twins and can therefore never be studied.

There are two different types of twins. Firstly there are DZ (dizygotic, or fraterna) twins, which appear when two eggs are fertilised at the same time by two sperm. Such twins are genetically no more alike than any other siblings. Secondly there are MZ (monozygotic, or identical) twins, which arise when one egg is fertilised by one sperm, the egg splitting after fertilisation. These twins are genetically identical and are always of the same sex. It is MZ twins that are important in these studies because their genetic framework is identical.

At the University of Minneapolis a special unit has been studying MZ twins for some time and many interesting results have been achieved. In the first instance it has been found that reuniting twins often unearths a set of amazing coincidences, that are difficult to explain by means of standard probability statistics.[9]

One amazing case is that of the 'giggle twins', Daphne and Barbara. They were born in 1939 in Hammersmith, London, and were immediately adopted into separate families, not meeting again until 1980. At the time of this meeting Daphne lived in Wakefield whilst Barbara was in Dover. It was found that both drank cold black coffee; both hated heights and seeing blood; both had no sense of direction; both suffered miscarriages with their first babies, then each had two boys followed by a girl; both fell downstairs, seriously injuring themselves at the age of fifteen; both used to read *My Weekly* then stopped; both tinted their grey hair with auburn; both had taken ballroom dancing lessons; both arrived at their reunion in a beige dress and brown velvet jacket. Both got very similar results in the tests carried out in the study, despite the fact that they had different family backgrounds.

A further example is the strange case of Dorothy and Bridget who were separated just after their birth in 1945 and reunited in 1979. Their list of coincidences is again a long one, and includes the following facts from their reunion. Both used the same perfume; both wore the same dresses at their weddings and carried the same flowers; both had cats called Tiger; both had had meningitis; both took piano lessons to the same grade and stopped after the same exam; Dorothy called her son Richard Andrew and her daughter Catherine Louise, Bridget called her son Andrew Richard and her daughter Karen Louise – she originally decided on Catherine Louise but was persuaded against it.

With strings of coincidences such as these, and there are many, many more examples,[10] it is easy to get the impression that perhaps not only is our intelligence very heavily dependent on genetics, but that many things in life have in some sense been predestined. The genetic link perhaps gives us some insight into why both members of a set of twins should suffer from the same medical problems, and even why they have particular likes and dislikes such as specific smells and foods. However, what appears to be truly astounding are the behavioural similarities. For example, with one pair of such twins it was found that they had both been married five times, while with another pair it was discovered that they were wearing exactly the same jewellery at their reunion.

The coincidences found through this study of twins have gone a long way to support the idea that inheritance plays some part in intelligent behaviour. However, in the past work of this type has been dogged by controversy. Russian research in the field was stopped from 1936 to the 1960s, as it was perceived to be at odds with communist egalitarian ideology. And the work of Sir Cyril Burt, which pointed to a clear link between inheritance and intelligence, was discredited by many leading psychologists in 1971. More recently, in 1966, the book The 'g' factor by Chris Brand, which again drew heavily on a genetic argument, was banned. In fact, since the 1960s, any research which has indicated that genes have the same sort of influence on our mental make-up as they do on our physical make-up, has been regarded as sinister.

The similarities found between twins can be grouped into three types:[11]

1. Anecdotal (e.g. similarities in names, cars, dress, holiday and sports)
2. Behavioural/psychological (e.g. similarities in jobs, fears, dreams)
3. Psychiatric (e.g. similarities in depression, drinking, weight, violence)

Often, although exhibiting such similarities, one twin is found to be more severe than the other. Indeed, in the womb twins must compete for nourishment and this can result in a considerable difference in size at birth.

It must not be thought that there are no differences between sets of separated twins, but it is the similarities that draw headlines and which are interesting in terms of research. And the most important similarities are those found in intelligence test results. When taking these tests many twins achieve the same score, make the same mistakes and finish at exactly the same time. Intriguingly, though, results are often more closely aligned when the twins are in separate rooms than when they are back to back in the same room. It has also been found that twins do much better at school if they are placed in separate classes.

What conclusions, then, can be drawn from all the studies on twins which have been carried out to date? Can we deduce anything about the genetic or environmental nature of intelligence?

The study with the largest number of twin sets included in it was that carried out by Sir Cyril Burt. Although, as I have said, he was discredited, his results have never been proved wrong. It has never been verified, however, that the twins he claimed to have tested, existed at all.

By 1966 Burt had presented results on well over 100 pairs of MZ twins, amongst them fifty-three pairs of MZ twins who had been separated at birth (the most important group), making it by far the most extensive study of its kind. He claimed the twins had been randomly placed in their adoptive homes and had had no further contact with each other since their birth. He showed a correlation of 0.77 in test results for the twins as a whole,[12] it being 0.86 for the separated MZ twins.

Burt's results showed the percentage split of nature/nurture to be about 80/20. This means that 80 per cent of an individual's intelligence can be put down to genetic inheritance, while the remaining 20 per cent is due to the environment. However, even if Burt's work cannot be believed it does not mean the opposite is true: that environment plays a greater part than genetic inheritance. As it happens Burt's study was only one in hundreds and, although his results were a little higher than average, others have not shown that much deviation. The results of John Loehlin's research in the 1970s were in fact remarkably similar.

In the Minneapolis study, mentioned earlier, results were pooled on a total of 122 pairs of separated MZ twins. The average IQ of the twins studied was 97, which is fairly typical of a normal population. The mean difference between the twins was 6.6 IQ points which correlates at 0.82, a fairly high result, and very similar to Burt's figure. This should indicate that genetics has a large part to play. However, it still cannot be concluded decisively if, as in many sets here, the twins were brought up in similar home backgrounds. In fact in this study it was found that the more separated the twins, the less alike were their IQs.[13]

Twin studies results generally seem to be more in favour of nature, but in all cases, bar Burt's, the complete set of criteria has not been adhered to. The twins have either been brought up in similar family backgrounds, or they have had further contact after adoption. A truly random separation and adoption, without any contact what-soever, has never been studied. Although no results are directly available which contradict those discussed, more conservative, and perhaps culturally motivated, estimates now put the nature/nurture split at 60/40 respectively.

CAN WE TEACH INTELLIGENCE?

The ratio of nature/nurture in intelligence raises the question: to what extent can intelligence be taught? If it can be taught, what does this mean? Is it simply a case of teaching an individual to think in a certain way? Or is intelligence far too complex an entity to be easily taught? A number of investigations have been carried out to discover whether or not children can be taught to think in a more intelligent manner.

One of the main such studies is the Instrumental Enrichment Programme, run by Reuven Feuerstein, the director of HadassanWizo in Canada and of the Institute and New Centre for the Development of Learning Potential in Israel. He claims that all children can be taught how to learn, that human intellect is extremely pliable and that cognitive development is deeply affected by the environment, particularly parental behaviour.

Feuerstein's ideas were put into practice in four schools in Bridgwater, Somerset. The key elements of this investigation were to make the children take notice of the teachers by giving learning a purpose or significance, and adding meaning and excitement to lessons. While there was little or no evidence to suggest that children's cognitive abilities were improved, pupils were shown to become more attentive and they participated more in the classes in question. This effectiveness, unfortunately, did not pass over to the other classes or life in general. The teachers involved did, however, become more confident and assertive, so some positive results came out of the programme.

Another study of this type was conducted on a group of disadvantaged children. An attempt was made to enrich their lives and counteract the effects of their relatively unstimulating environment. Again this investigation showed mixed results.[14] Up to the age of three or four years old there appeared to have been quite positive effects on the group in comparison with contemporaries. By the age of twelve, however, the effects of this enrichment were only slight.

So what, if any, positive results can enrichment programmes provide? As we have seen in these two examples, long-term effects are rare. Although intellectual improvement is apparent while individuals remain in the programme, these positive effects seem to slowly seep away afterwards.

THE TRUTH ABOUT INTELLIGENCE?

The main point is that both genetics and environment play a part in an individual's intelligence. The relative effect of each of these areas is, whether we like it or not, still not only a matter of debate, but also a mystery which may be impossible to solve. What does this mean to our investigation?

I feel that everyone is an individual. While genetics and the environment both help to make up an individual's intelligence, it is the whole that is important. The environment may have a greater or lesser influence on one individual than on another. Attempting to apply exact percentages to everyone is plainly daft. This said, however, results obtained to date clearly indicate that genetics/nature has by far the biggest effect.

It is rather disturbing to think that hereditary factors play a greater role in intelligence than the environment in which we grow up. It implies that we will have little success in influencing the genetic make-up we have been given. And results from studies, such as Feuerstein's Enrichment Programme, seem to back up this idea. So, is there anything we can do to bolster what nature has given us? We shall turn to this question in Chapter 7. But first we need to look at the different ways that have been found to measure and assess intelligence.

5

TESTING INTELLIGENCE

IT IS HUMAN NATURE TO COMPARE and compete. Indeed, our survival on earth depends on our ability to compete and win. This competition has not only been between humans and other animals, and now humans and machines, but also between groups and individuals within our own species. Which ethnic group is the most intelligent? Which sex is the most intelligent? Which person in the office is the most intelligent? Which family member is the most intelligent?

But perhaps the way we go about this ranking is unfair. After all, it's hardly sensible to judge someone's intelligence on the basis of something which may be outside that individual's culture or experience.

To illustrate this point, look at the following questions:

1. Calculate t in terms of x.

$$\frac{dx}{dt} = (3x^2 + 2e^{-x})^{-1}$$

2. Which is the odd one out?

Tom Cruise, Brad Pitt, Michael Caine, Dustin Hoffman.

3. Which is the odd one out?

Ileum, clavicle, duodenum, oesophagus.

To answer the first question it is imperative to have knowledge, to a high level, in mathematics. The second assumes some familiarity with English and American film stars, while the third requires you to have some knowledge of human biological systems. In all these examples a basic understanding of what is being asked is required before any attempt can be made to answer them. Clearly, context, culture and environment are all directly linked with assessment of intelligence, whether in humans, animals or machines.

When comparing the abilities of individuals, how can their respective intellects by fairly ranked? One person may be incredibly good at an activity; their opponent may not be so good at that particular activity but perhaps display a greater ability at a different subject. Does knowledge of one particular subject show more intelligence than that of another? Is a person who can do mental arithmetic quickly and accurately more intelligent than a person who can remember historical facts?

We might, for instance, conclude that an American is more intelligent than a Russian (who has never experienced the American way of life), based on answers given when questioned on names of American baseball players or American toothpaste. This latter scenario could never happen; could it? Would one group of humans persecute another for simply not understanding or displaying knowledge of a culture they had never experienced? Surely we as humans are not so short-sighted, or so competitive, that we would ever resort to biased and unfair means. Or would we?

It is only when all differences in culture and social background have been removed that a reasonably fair test of intelligence can be applied. In reality this has proved impossible. Every individual experiences life differently. Events in one person's life are different from those in another's, just as the likes and dislikes of one person are different from those of another. Every individual's approach to tests of intelligence is therefore different. If a test contains questions which fall within one person's experience, but outside another's, can the first individual really be said to be more intelligent than the second simply because he has come across this scenario before? I do not believe so. We must therefore conclude that it is not possible to compare two individuals and categorically state that one has a higher intelligence than the other.

It is easy to say that there is no fair way to compare the intelligence of different individuals, but we all know that it happens. There are many different types of test which claim to measure intelligence accurately. These include psychometric tests, spatial awareness tests, and many others. But, for the purposes of this book, we are going to pay most attention to the best known of all, IQ tests. According to the 1995 edition of the *Oxford English Dictionary*, 'A person's IQ is a number denoting the ratio of their intelligence to the statistical norm.' This definition reflects the popular view that IQ is indeed a measure of a person's intelligence. At present an IQ of 100 is seen as average. Possess a figure above this and you are seen as more intelligent; below this and you are thought to be less intelligent. Anyone with an IQ above 150 is thought, by some, to be in the range of genius.

THE HISTORY OF THE IQ TEST

The IQ test was first formulated by Alfred Binet in 1904, when the intention was to use it to identify children who would struggle in a normal school environment. Binet's original work, on intelligence, had followed the conventions of the time, being largely based on skull size. After undertaking a number of unsuccessful studies in this area, however, he became disillusioned with this approach. When he was asked to devise a new test for schoolchildren he decided to concentrate on the study of mental faculties such as memory, comprehension, imagination, moral understanding, motor skills and attention, and use them as guides to intelligence.

Binet employed an experimental approach to devise the activities which made up the prototype of what we now know as the IQ test. The final version of Binet's original test had thirty parts and was designed to be taken by children between three and twelve years of age. A child taking the test worked through the sections in sequence until they reached a point where they could no longer complete the activities. The number at this point was then said to be the 'mental age' of the child concerned. The intellectual level of the child was calculated by subtracting this mental age from the child's actual age.

This formula was eventually changed by William Stern, a German psychologist, to represent the ratio between mental age and chronological age and is known as the Intelligence Quotient or IQ:

$$IQ = \frac{Mental\ Age}{Chronological\ Age} \times 100$$

Binet's work was undertaken to find a way to predict the scholastic ability of children. He never claimed that the results of his tests would give an absolute measure of intelligence. He recognised that intelligence was far more complex and diverse than could simply be indicated by a single number. He was of the opinion that the tests he had produced were only useful in predicting those children who would be under-achievers: 'We are of the opinion that the most valuable application of our scale will not be for the normal subject, but instead for the inferior degrees of intelligence.' Binet's worst fear was that the work he had done would cause particular children to be seen as unintelligent purely as the result of a test. This fear was well founded.

Binet's test was quickly picked up and used around the world. It made the strongest impact in the United States where it underwent a series of alterations and was used for many years as a base upon which to structure society. One of the most important changes was made by Lewis Terman. In 1916 Terman, from Stanford University, revised Binet's tests to include a wider variety of tasks, involving reasoning and vocabulary. In doing so, he brought the total number of individual activities included in the test to ninety. This revised edition became known as the Stanford-Binet test and all the IQ tests which followed have been based on it.

It was felt by many that the Stanford-Binet test, whilst being useful for testing children, did not give good results when it came to testing adults. David Wechsler therefore produced, in 1939, the Wechsler Adult Intelligent Scale (WAIS), which is solely for use on adults. Many modifications were made to the Stanford-Binet test, including the use of general knowledge questions, completing jigsaws and solving mazes. In recent years these have been expanded further to produce psychometric testing which also tries to indicate 'why' an individual thinks in a certain way.

THE PROBLEMS OF IQ TESTING

Nowadays the use of such tests has begun to be questioned, for two main reasons: firstly the possibility that the tests are culturally biased, and secondly the possibility that they don't actually constitute a valid measure of intelligence. The foundation for these criticisms is the Theory of Subjective Intelligence, discussed in Chapter 1.

In the early IQ tests certain groups were often favoured due to the subjective nature of the tests. For example, results from IQ tests were used to 'prove' that men were more intelligent than women. It is very easy to insert bias into the questions employed in these tests, without the tester even being aware of it, in order to uphold situations which already exist. In reality, it is impossible to test a person's general knowledge without taking into account their individual make-up.

Binet's original tests were conducted in a one-to-one situation – the tester and the tested. As these tests became popular, however, the testing of more and more individuals was required and this personal approach became impractical. With the advent of mass testing there was a shift away from simply trying to sort out the bright from the dull. Now the aim was to give each person a number that would be indicative of their intelligence. IQ test results could then be used to provide some people with opportunities, and others not, as the information gained was thought to show what individuals would be capable of doing with the rest of their lives.

One of the most famous examples of this application of IQ testing occurred in the UK from the mid-1940s through to the late 1960s. During this time all eleven-year-old children took tests in arithmetic, verbal reasoning and English, known as the 'eleven plus'. The results of these tests were used to determine which school each child could go on to. Those with the highest marks went on to high-achieving grammar schools, while those that 'failed' went to secondary modern schools. However these exam results did not only affect which school was to be attended after the age of eleven, but quite often had an effect on the rest of a child's life. Those who had attended a better school were given a better education and were therefore able to get better jobs, while those who did not do so well attended schools which were, perhaps, not as good. This meant that their standard of education and therefore their job prospects were lowered.

The problems, which Binet had pointed out years before, associated with labelling people with a fixed level of intelligence, were fully realised. How many children's lives were adversely affected by 'failing' the eleven plus, reducing their self-worth and preventing them from fulfilling their potential?

How Valid are IQ Tests?

Evidence shows that performance in Stanford-Binet type IQ tests gives a good indication of how well an individual will perform in school examinations, but does it really show how intelligent an individual is? Many people appear to assume that performance in school is a measure of intelligence. On this basis it follows that any test which can predict an individual's performance at school reasonably accurately must also give an indication of that person's intelligence.

However, it is well-known that some people cope better with the stress of examinations than others. Some individuals can be overwhelmed by nervous energy, while others thrive on it. The way in which this nervous stress is dealt with can have a direct effect on the results gained in any examination situation. Those who find it difficult to cope often obtain results which do not reflect their true potential. So, are you less intelligent if you have difficulty coping with examination situations? This makes as little sense as saying someone is less intelligent if they are scared of heights.

In recent years schools have started trying to place less emphasis on examinations, and more on work done during the year. In this way mini-tests, homework and practical assignments are taken into account. This gives something of an advantage to those who put more effort into their work, or who spend more time on it. While there can be no strong objections to students receiving marks for such coursework, the links between such marks and an individual's intelligence can certainly be questioned. Is an individual who puts in five minutes effort to get 90 per cent of a problem correct less intelligent than someone else who takes five days to achieve 92 per cent of the same problem? Putting emphasis on practical abilities is important, to some degree, and this is something which Stanford-Binet tests, along with most school examinations, fail to do.

The link between IQ tests and performance in school examinations is a circular one. The early IQ tests were intended to predict examination performance, and the new, more recently introduced, tests are compared with older tests and school performance in order to validate them. If a new test provides a better correlation with school performance than the original Stanford-Binet test it is regarded as a better test. However, as we do not know whether the original tests actually predicted intelligence levels in the first place, is it right to use them as a validity measure? Likewise, the validity of school examinations is brought into question if the performances achieved in them vary significantly from those achieved by the same individuals in IQ tests. But should this be the case?

IQ tests and school examinations therefore appear to be in a spiral, supporting each other in what they are testing and in how the tests are set out. To be in a position to change the tests an individual will almost surely have already, themselves, succeeded at both this type of IQ test and in the related academic examinations. Interestingly, while there is a high correlation between IQ test performance and job status, there is a surprisingly low correlation between IQ test results and actual performance in an occupation. Despite this, the selection of employees is frequently made on the basis of IQ and/or educational results.[2]

THE MISUSE OF IQ TESTS

It was in America that the misuse of Binet's test began in earnest. The tests were actually introduced to the USA by H. H. Goddard, who immediately claimed that the results indicated innate intelligence.

The USA at this time was experiencing mass immigration from all areas of Europe and its own native population was also beginning to grow. It was thought by many that with this population growth came a decrease in overall intelligence level, due to the large numbers of low intelligence immigrants and the increasing numbers of America's own 'feeble-minded' population.

Intelligence was then believed to be solely hereditary. On this basis, Goddard felt that the genes which caused a lack of intelligence should be eliminated, and the only way to do this was to stop those who carry such genes (the 'feeble-minded') from bearing children.

Goddard said: 'If both parents are feeble-minded, all children will be feeble-minded. It is obvious that such matings should not be allowed. It is perfectly clear that no feeble-minded person should ever be allowed to marry or to become a parent.'[3] Whilst intelligent individuals could control their sexual emotions, it was felt that the feeble-minded, rather like other animals, were not so restrained. Goddard went on, 'They are not only lacking in control but they are lacking often in the perception of moral qualities . . . there are two proposals: the first is colonisation, the second is sterilisation.'[4]

Goddard favoured the 'colonisation' of the feeble-minded (that is, placing them in special institutions where males and females could be segregated). Perhaps it was no coincidence that Goddard himself ran such an institution in New Jersey, which cost a great deal to maintain.

It is also important to note the vast numbers of people being classified by Goddard as feeble-minded. Having applied the Binet test to several sets of immigrants, he claimed that 79 per cent of Italians, 80 per cent of Hungarians, 83 per cent of Jews and 87 per cent of Russians seeking immigration were 'feeble-minded'.

Goddard applied these tests, steeped in American culture, to foreigners who had just arrived in the country, after a long sea voyage, many having never attended school in their lives. This was an example of Subjective Intelligence in the extreme. The possibility that the tests were biased against foreigners was dismissed by Goddard. Although he admitted that on the one hand 'drawing a memorised design' might well be difficult for those who had never held a pencil before, on the other reciting sixty words of your own language within a three-minute period should not be too taxing even allowing for differences in culture and possible nervousness, fear, confusion and tiredness in those being tested.[5] These bizarre results only show, yet again, that humans need to be tested in a way that is appropriate to their culture, background and race in order to have any hope of getting a realistic indication of their intelligence.

Yet, quite incredibly, on the basis of Goddard's evidence and other supporting reports, several states in the USA passed laws mandating the involuntary sterilisation of thousands diagnosed as 'feeble-minded'. For example, between 1924 and 1972, as many as 7500 individuals, classified as 'feeble-minded', were sterilised in the state of Virginia. In many cases people were not even aware that they had been sterilised. In 1928 Doris Buck was told that she had to have an operation to have her appendix removed. Later in life, after spending years trying to conceive, she found out that the operation had actually been to sever her fallopian tubes.[6]

Was there any scientific basis for this sterilisation programme? Assuming that at least some percentage of an individual's intelligence is due to genetic inheritance, it can be shown that the offspring of individuals of high intelligence, in terms of IQ test results, are more likely to be of above average intelligence themselves, while those with parents of low intelligence are more likely to be below the intellectual average. This would mean that the sterilisation of adults below the average intelligence level of a society would tend, over time, to increase the intellectual level of that society. For this to work, however, one needs an accurate indicator of intelligence. For Americans in the early twentieth century this was of course the IQ test.

Although sterilisation of the 'feeble-minded' was acceptable in America eighty years ago it is certainly not acceptable nowadays. The result of this, whether we like it or not, is a downward pull on the overall intellectual norm because of the number of less intelligent individuals having offspring. This is further compounded if we believe studies such as that of Herrnstein and Murray (*The Bell Curve*, 1994),[7] which states that individuals of particularly low intelligence tend, on average, to have far more children than those of higher intelligence. In the distant past many of these offspring would not have reached maturity, but now – due to much improved medical and social facilities, in the Western world at least – relatively few offspring die in childhood.

With greater numbers of children surviving to adulthood, and the fact that humans are tending, on average, to live longer, the knock-on effect is that the human population of the world is increasing rapidly. China, which has a huge overpopulation problem, has, in recent years, begun to limit all parenting couples to one child only. This will not only have the effect of generally reducing its overall population but it will also have, if Herrnstein and Murray are to be believed, a positive effect on the average level of intelligence in China. There will no longer be a downward shift on the intellectual norm because the number of children born to all ranges of intelligence should be roughly equal.

THE YERKES TEST FOR AMERICAN ARMY RECRUITS

The first group testing was carried out by Robert M. Yerkes for entry to the United States Army during the First World War. This test was taken by 1.75 million individuals, and a number of controversial conclusions were drawn from the results. Firstly the average mental age of white American adults was found to be 13 (just above the level for 'feeble-mindedness'). Secondly the average mental age for Russians was found to be 11.34, Italians 11.01 and Poles 10.74. Finally, it was apparent that the black Americans were at the bottom of the heap, with an average mental age of only 10.41. This meant that 89 per cent of black Americans and 37 per cent of white Americans could be classified as morons.[8]

This information was greeted with horror amongst American upper-class and political circles, and helped the cause of those who wished to impose curbs on immigration. If the average intelligence of a native American was so low the country did not need an influx of slow-witted immigrants to pull it down further. The figures obtained by Yerkes were looked upon as accurate; no allowance was made for differences in environmental or cultural backgrounds which may have explained why immigrant or black populations tended to achieve lower scores.

In recent years both Yerkes and his testing methods have, quite rightly, come in for much criticism. The most common charge is that his tests were biased and required extensive knowledge of American culture in order to do well. For example, look at the following questions which were actually included in the tests:

1. 'Crisco is a: patent medicine, disinfectant, toothpaste, food product.'
2. 'Christy Matthewson is famous as a: writer, artist, baseball player, comedian.'[9]

Do you know the answers? Imagine yourself to be a new immigrant from a non-English speaking country; would you stand a better chance? Could you have even understood the questions under those circumstances?

Perhaps when you read my own sample questions in Chapter 1,

in the discussion on Subjective Intelligence, you may have found them too subjective. How could anyone, except me, answer them? But how different are they from the questions just quoted in terms of the cultural references contained within them?

Yerkes' pictorial questions contained similar biases. Examples included: adding a filament to a bulb, a rivet to a pocket knife, and a baseball to a pitcher's hand. These were certainly problematic for people whose country of origin may not have been as technologically advanced or as steeped in baseball as America. One specific story tells of a Sicilian recruit who added a crucifix to a house rather than the 'correct' chimney. This answer was marked wrong even though it was a familiar sight in his homeland.[10]

When Yerkes' results were analysed two main peaks in performance were found, one at a middle value and the other at zero. The proportion of results at zero was especially high, one particular set giving 40 per cent of all scores at zero. Instead of concluding that many individuals simply did not understand the instructions, supporters of the test assumed that those who had scored zero possessed a very low level of intelligence.

Yerkes was convinced that genetics and intelligence were directly linked. He therefore saw his results as extremely important factors in deciding from which countries immigration should be curtailed. He thought it was a person's lack of intelligence which caused them to become poor and unhealthy.

Of 348 men who scored below the norm in one test only one had ever attended college and only ten had attended high school.[11] It did not, however, follow, in the mind of Yerkes, that it was attending school which caused a person to become more intelligent. Instead he thought that men with more innate intelligence spent more time at school. Interestingly in my own lectures at Reading I have noticed that those students who regularly attend my lectures do much better in examinations, on average, than those with a poor attendance.

Approaching this situation from Yerkes' standpoint clearly indicates that those with more innate intelligence regularly attend my lectures!

In subsequent tests Yerkes found that for the foreign recruits average test scores increased consistently with the number of years residence in the USA. This could have been put down to an increased familiarity with American culture and therefore the ability to do better at the tests. However, Yerkes instead suggested, 'It might be, for instance that the more intelligent immigrants succeed and therefore remain in this country.'[12]

The army data had an immediate effect on the political debate on the restrictions in immigration. As Brigham, Yerkes' right-hand man, put it, 'Immigration should not only be restrictive but highly selective.' He went on, 'The really important steps are looking toward the prevention of the continued propagation of defective strains in the present population.'[13] Clearly, the idea of weeding out the less intelligent members of the population was still very much in the air, as well as stopping such immigrants in the first place.

Perhaps the feeling in the USA at the time is best summed up by Henry Fairfield Osborn, who was trustee of Columbia University and President of the American Museum of National History. In 1923 he wrote, 'in reference to the Yerkes' test results and the First World War:

I believe those tests were worth what the war cost, even in human life, if they served to show clearly to our people the lack of intelligence in our country, and the degrees of intelligence of different races who are coming to us, in a way which no one can say is the result of prejudice.' He continued, 'We have learnt once and for all that the Negro is not like us, so in regard to many races and sub-races in Europe we learned that some [Jews] which we had believed possessed an order of intelligence perhaps superior to ours, were inferior.'[14]

It is worth pointing out that some 8.5 million people died in the First World War.[15] How can anyone really say that it was worth those deaths simply to show the intelligence of a society, based on tests which even today we are not sure of?

Mounting pressure in the USA resulted in the Immigration Restriction Act of 1924, which limited the inflow of immigrants to 2 per cent of that recorded from each nation in 1890. The effect was widespread. In the 1930s, many Jewish refugees sought to emigrate in anticipation of the Holocaust but found the door to the USA firmly closed.

The question remains, do IQ test results give an indication of an individual's intelligence (as Brigham thought), or do they merely indicate the score achieved on a test? It is apparent that Binet's original tests, and the subsequent Army tests of Yerkes, provided the basis for a general concept of hereditary intelligence. They also created a basis, contrary to Binet's wishes, for the widespread testing and ranking of children in relation to their perceived intelligence, testing which is still going on today.

I have looked closely at IQ testing in the USA during the last century for a number of reasons. One of these was to show just how subjective humans can be when considering what are signs of intelligence and what are not. The tests considered here were clearly biased towards American culture. If the test results showed anything then they indicated each individual's knowledge, at that time, of American culture, and little more. Another reason for looking at the situation in depth was to indicate the strange conclusions people can come to, as a result of such tests, and the important decisions that can be subsequently made. For example, because individual A did better than individual B, individual A was also felt to be able to produce offspring in a reasonable way, whereas individual B could not.

What is considered an intelligent act in one human group may well have little or no value in another. Intelligence must necessarily, therefore, be subjective, although we may simply not realise that we are imposing such subjectivity when applying a test. Between humans we have natural cultural biases, language being a prime example. When we compare human intelligence with that of other creatures, however, this subjectivity is much more in evidence. For example if we conclude that a machine is not 'genuinely' intelligent because it does not 'understand' English,[16] this is an even more extreme example of subjectivity gone mad than was the case with the American Army questions.

CULTURE-FREE IQ TESTS?

Attempts have been made, over the years, to remove as much cultural basis as possible from IQ tests. Consider, for example, the following questions:[17]

1. Insert the missing number:

18	25	4
16	20	3
6	15	?

2. Select the correct figure from the six numbered ones:

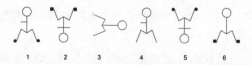

For question one the expected answer is 3 (subtract the figure in the second row from that in the first and multiply by 3 to get the third row figure). While for question two you should have chosen figure 1.

It is certainly true that neither of these questions requires a knowledge of politics, literature or language, with all the cultural leanings they contain. Nevertheless they do require a knowledge of a particular human culture. In question one, the base 10 is assumed. If we look at the same question to the base 9 or 16, the problem is completely different, with a different answer. Question two meanwhile uses a simple code system to move from pictures to numbers. The ability to recognise and extrapolate on such a coding system is a culturally learnt technique.

For many people, the strategies needed to understand and answer such questions may feel like second nature; they may question how anyone could look at them differently. But this is because they are truly part of the culture from which these questions originate. Others looking at these questions may well not be able to relate to them at all. In this case their cultural upbringing was different.

Importantly, other animals and insects would be unable to answer these questions, but does that make them less intelligent than a human who can answer the question? A computer, on the other hand, may well be able to answer the questions quickly and easily; does this make a computer more intelligent than a human who cannot answer them?

TAKING IQ TESTS WITH A PINCH OF SALT

While test results today may not, as far as we know, directly cause an individual's application for immigration to be turned down, or result in their forced sterilisation, such results can still have a profound effect. Poor tests results can easily label some individuals as inferior,[18] affecting their feelings of self-worth and motivation, as well as removing career opportunities. Conversely, a good score can give an individual an inflated view of their own importance and enable them to achieve things which perhaps they would not have thought of attempting before.

Throughout history people have tried to obtain a measure of each individual's overall intelligence. Links have been drawn between physical characteristics, such as skull size or reaction time, and intelligence. In the twentieth century psychological testing rose to prominence, but we are still left wondering how far such tests go in showing our actual intelligence and how far they simply record our performance in a particular test at a particular time.

More recent tests, such as psychometric analysis, have attempted to broaden the range of abilities under consideration and thus give a more accurate picture of individual intelligence. However, the range of mental attributes that give an indication of intelligence is extremely difficult to quantify. Hence any IQ value will, at best, indicate only an individual's performance in certain areas that can be thought of as requiring intelligence.

In view of all its shortcomings, does IQ testing help us in our quest to identify exactly what intelligence is? Is it ever possible to indicate an individual's intelligence by means of a single test score? Intelligence is the multi-faceted mental performance of an individual; if we wish to measure it perhaps we need to assess a whole series of attributes across the mental spectrum. A single IQ can only ever be a broad average value. An individual's IQ test results should be treated simply as the results of a test, or at best as a possible indication of scholastic performance. They should not, at present, be regarded as giving an accurate indication of an individual's intelligence.

Nowadays, to join a number of societies you need to do particularly well at IQ tests. The most famous example is MENSA, which has a worldwide membership. To become a member you must be able to achieve, on a standard IQ test, a higher score than 98 per cent of the general population. Being a member of MENSA has always supposedly indicated that you are highly intelligent and makes you almost intimidating to the rest of the population. Yet why should this be the case when past experience has taught us that IQ tests do not truly measure intelligence? Maybe it is time to take the claims of MENSA for what they are – a joke.

So where do we go from here? If IQ tests, while not measuring intelligence in all its aspects, do give an indication of some elements of an individual's performance, then perhaps they can still be useful to us. But we need to consider how our intelligence differs, and whether our social background or race are linked to our intelligence. If genetics has anything to do with it then surely racial differences exist, but can we draw that conclusion and get away with it politically?

6

FACTORS
INFLUENCING
INTELLIGENCE

NTELLIGENCE TODAY IS A highly valued commodity. We all like
to think of ourselves as more intelligent than the next person and
we generally feel uncomfortable in the presence of someone who
makes us feel less intelligent than themselves. This way of thinking
makes us easy victims of the media, who love to promote stories such
as 'cycling makes you more intelligent', or 'going on holiday
makes you less intelligent'. How many of us feel we can ignore such
stories? How many of us, if offered a special elixir which was
guaranteed to make us 10 per cent more intelligent, would refuse to
take it?

In the real world, however, how do everyday things affect our
intelligence? How does our mode of upbringing, and the environment
in which we live as unborn babies, children and adults, affect our
intelligence? What about the things we eat, or our general lifestyle?

Does our class, race or gender have any bearing on our intelligence? In this chapter I will cut through the prejudices surrounding these issues and report on the truth in full, no matter how uncomfortable it might be.

Unfortunately, in doing this, we immediately face the problem of measuring intelligence, with all its subjective, cultural and complex implications. As a first step we can refer to IQ tests. Despite their shortcomings discussed in the previous chapter they do provide a window on intelligence of sorts. We can also look at academic and subsequent personal and professional achievements as related evidence.

LIFESTYLE

As we saw earlier, it is believed nowadays that a person's intelligence is partly due to environmental factors and partly to genetics, in what is most commonly quoted as a 40/60 per cent split (environment/inheritance). If this is the case then we each have 40 per cent of our intelligence – quite a large percentage – that is directly influenced by our actions and lifestyle.

Human mental development can be likened to physical development. Physically, we grow and develop to our peak of performance somewhere in our late teens. After this point we must maintain this level by taking regular exercise. Exactly the same is true from a mental perspective. Children grow physically at different rates, putting on a spurt for a few months and then slowing down. There is a similar process mentally. The brain is, after all, a physical thing, which develops as we learn. It also needs exercising in later life in order to keep it in shape.

As children, we were constantly stretched, physically and mentally, both at school and at home, as we learnt new things and played new games. But, as adults, what mental exercise do we get? It is only after we are convinced by experts that physical exercise is a necessity that some of us take up swimming, aerobics or running in order to tone our bodies and maintain a level of fitness. There is, however, no one telling us to do the same with our minds. Think of your daily routine: you probably get up, have breakfast, go to work, come home, have an evening meal, sit down, relax and then go to bed. Many of us stay in the same job year in year out; what effect can this lack of new mental stimulation be having?

Recent research suggests that, in order to stay at the peak of mental awareness throughout our lives, we must begin to exercise our brains as well as our bodies. Instead of watching soap operas and sit coms in the evening, perhaps we should spend some time strengthening our minds. Activities which are thought to do this are jigsaw puzzles, crosswords, chess and the like. Perhaps we should begin to indulge in such pursuits every day.

MALE AND FEMALE BRAINS

Physically men and women are different. That is undeniable, as is the fact that their priorities and ways of perceiving the world are also different. If, however, it is suggested that intelligence may differ between the sexes then the cries of protest immediately drown out the debate. Yet there is some compelling evidence that needs to be explored.

For example, even a few hours after birth, girls and boys react differently to certain stimuli. Tests have shown that girls are more sensitive to touch than boys; so much so that the most sensitive boy is not as sensitive as the least sensitive girl. Other studies on infants and young children show that baby girls spend almost twice as long maintaining eye contact with adults, and fix longer on a talking adult than do their male counterparts.[1] Instead boys appear to be much more interested in visual stimuli and are generally far more active than girls, being just as content communicating with toys as with people. Girl babies tend to be much more aware of people, in terms of communication and other aspects of behaviour. For instance, unlike baby boys, they can select photos of adults they have seen from a very early age.

Throughout their growing lives boys and girls behave different-ly but fairly stereotypically within their genders. This has to have a direct effect on their intelligence. With the subjective nature of IQ tests, it is therefore fairly easy to bias tests more towards girls or boys. In recent years it has been reported that, in the UK, girls have been performing better at primary and secondary school than boys. This has been followed by a higher proportion of girls now gaining entry to universities, which has been reported by parts of the media as women being 'brainier' than men. Under certain circumstances, this may be true. But a much more likely answer is that girls are either trying harder than boys, or that the testing being carried out in UK schools has shifted subjectively in favour of girls.

Despite this recent trend in examination results, overall IQ test results are not generally significantly different between men and women. Having said this, the two sexes tend to do well in different areas within the test. Men usually achieve better results in performance-related spatial tasks, whereas women do better at verbal tasks. This can be partly explained by environmental and social fac-tors, but on the whole it would appear to be genetic factors which cause these differences.

Studies of brain structure have shown that there are significant differences between men and women. Men's brains are, on average, 15 per cent larger than women's, although this feature can be relat-ed to their larger body size. Women, meanwhile, have brains which are more densely populated with neurons. Other research has shown that men tend to concentrate particular activities on one side of the brain or the other, while women, more often than not, use both sides of their brain. The structure of a woman's brain backs up this observation, as it has a much larger corpus callosum than a man's (the corpus callosum is essentially a bunch of fibres which links the left and right sides of the brain). This makes it seem likely that there is much more communication between the two hemispheres of a woman's brain than is possible in a man's.

Historically, immense importance has been placed on differences in brain size. For example, in Germany in 1911 the minimum requirement for a professor was a head circumference of 52 centimetres. Herr Bayerthal, a leading German medical physicist, wrote at the time: 'Under 52 centimetres you cannot expect an intellectual performance of any significance, while under 50.5 centimetres no normal intelligence can be expected.'[2] Women were, for the most part, completely excluded from consideration, as we can see from Bayerthal's further comment: 'We do not have to ask for the head circumference of women of genius – they do not exist.'[3]

Around the same time Gustave Le Bon, a French scientist, noted that women had brains which were closer in size to those of gorillas than they were to men. He felt that men's superiority over women was 'so obvious that no one can contest it for a moment.'[4] He warned of a potential dire future in which 'misunderstanding the inferior occupations which nature has given her, women leave the home to take part in our battles; on that day a social revolution will begin and everything that maintains the sacred ties of family will disappear.'[5] We appear to have been living in Le Bon's 'dire' future for quite some time.

Clearly, when comparing the mental processes of men and women, we need to realise and understand that there are differences, but that these differences are slight. And we must also understand that there is nothing wrong with these differences existing; in fact, in evolutionary and survival terms it would appear to be quite sensible and practical for them to be present. In the last thirty years however, there has been a shift towards ignoring these differences with the result that, in order to be politically correct, we now proclaim ourselves to be the same.

I feel that this approach is wrong. We should acknowledge these differences and realise that they do not mean that one sex is inferior to the other. We should stop using the subjective nature of intelligence to hide or exaggerate these variations and simply admit that men and women think differently. Perhaps we should see men and women's mental processes as complementing each other, rather than attempting to set one up as better or worse than the other.

FOOD FOR THOUGHT?

As far as our intelligence is concerned, it could be argued that the differences between men and women have been blown out of all proportion. Other factors may not only have far more significance, but could also be things that we can directly influence and change. One aspect that immediately springs to mind is nutrition. How does what we eat and drink affect the way we think? Are there any particular foodstuffs which we can eat that will make us more intelligent?

In terms of physical capabilities, certain foods have been found to result in improved performance. For example, Arsenal Football Club's Championship/Cup Double wining side of 1998 was restricted to a daily diet of boiled vegetables and boiled chicken – an almost zero fat intake.[6] Is the same true of our mental processes? Can a specialised diet lead to improved mental performance?

Research into this subject has shown that the balance of a diet is very important. Results found indicate that different combinations of food groups seem to have different effects on the way in which neurons operate. The proportions of carbohydrates (such as those found in potatoes and pasta) relative to proteins (such as meat, fish and nuts) have significant effects on the way in which plasma and amino acids balance in the brain and the resultant synthesis that goes on. For example, a diet high in carbohydrate has the effect of increasing sleepiness, reducing mental performance and alertness, decreasing sensitivity to pain, decreasing mood swings and causing less aggressive behaviour. Other results have shown that consuming a meal high in fat causes the slowing down of the thought processes and leads to drowsiness. A high glucose intake, however, has been found to enhance both learning and memory.

Further research in this area has claimed that vitamin and mineral supplements can also have a substantial effect. In a carefully controlled study, carried out in 1988, by David Benton and Gwilym Roberts, thirty Welsh schoolchildren were used to test this hypothesis. These children were split into three different groups: those who were given no tablets; those who were given a placebo (in this case a sugar pill); and those who were given a vitamin C or mineral supplement. The trial ran for nine months, and the children were made to sit IQ tests at the beginning and end of this period. It was found that, on average, the group taking the supplement gained 8 points on their non-verbal test scores, while the verbal scores and the scores of the other children stayed roughly constant. A similar experiment on 600 children in California resulted in a 4-point increase over a thirteen-week period for those children on the supplement.[7]

In P. G. Wodehouse's *The Inimitable Jeeves* Jeeves doted on fish, believing that eating it would improve his intellect. Recent research[8] indicates that there may well be some truth in this, although the results are far from conclusive. Meanwhile caffeine intake has been found to improve the cognitive processes[9] as well as reducing the frequently experienced post-lunch dip in performance. We look further into this in research detailed in Chapter 7.

The obvious conclusion to be drawn from these results is that adding a vitamin supplement to your diet will always have a positive effect on your IQ. However, while a person from a deprived background with a poor diet will probably improve their IQ test results after the introduction of extra vitamins, a person who enjoys a well-balanced diet may not notice any change at all. It is therefore difficult to accurately predict whether any improvement will occur in a particular individual. However, it does show that there are links between social background, income and intelligence.

LEAD POLLUTION

Another aspect of life thought to affect intelligence, which also relates to an individual's social and cultural background, is pollution. In many countries pollutants in the air around us, the water we drink and the food we eat have been seen to cause health problems. For example, asthma now affects a far greater proportion of people than it did fifty years ago, while cases of childhood leukaemia have also dramatically increased. Could the same environmental factors damage our intelligence by affecting the way our brains work?

Of particular interest in this field is the question of lead poisoning. Numerous studies have been carried out to investigate the link between lead and intelligence, particularly because it has been found that lead alters the release processes for neurotransmitters and so definitely affects brain operation.

Many of these studies, however, failed to reveal any link between lead and IQ test results. On average, the results show that approximately doubling a person's lead burden (a pretty substantial amount) reduces IQ by a mere 1 or 2 points.[10] Because it is difficult to exclude other social and cultural effects, it is difficult to draw precise conclusions from the results found. For instance, it may initially appear that children of lower IQ have an increased lead uptake, but does this mean that they do things that cause them to be more likely to take up lead? For example they may play near busy roads and obtain water from lead pipes.

Other studies have concentrated not on the effects of lead on children already born, but rather the effects on the human foetus and/or babies shortly after birth. Again none of the results conclusively indicated any link with IQ. The only thing that can be said with any certainty is that the body burden of lead has an important, but relatively small influence on an individual's intellectual performance. Large amounts of lead, along with carbon monoxide, can cause a reduction in IQ, reading disabilities, behavioural problems, memory loss and long-term effects on the nervous system. The use of the word 'can' here is significant, as it indicates that many children will experience no effect or only a slight effect. From a purely IQ perspective, it would perhaps be better to concentrate efforts on supplying children with a balanced, nutritious diet, rather than trying to reduce pollution.

INTELLIGENCE IN BABIES

We have seen that certain factors can affect our intelligence as children and adults, but can the same be true of babies and unborns? Does what our mothers eat, drink, or do while pregnant cause our brains to develop in a certain direction. Or does the way our parents treat us when first born and as toddlers cause positive or negative effects?

Much research has focused on comparing breast-fed and bottle-fed babies. Numerous studies have shown that breast-fed babies are more content, well adjusted, and, on average, more intelligent than those who were bottle-fed. But can differences in intelligence really arise from simply sucking a mother's breast? Is it the nutritional value of the milk which is the key? Or are there other factors more closely related to social and environmental background in general?

Adults who were breast-fed as babies usually achieve slightly higher IQ scores than those who were either bottle-fed or both bottle and breast-fed. Further studies show that these positive effects are multiplied the longer breast-feeding continues. More recently, however, researchers have begun to argue that these differences in IQ disappear when other factors are taken into account.

The main reason why breast-feeding is said to be better for babies involves the nutritional make-up of breast milk. It is claimed that there are certain elements – such as fatty acids – that aid brain development, which are not present in milk formula. Arguments against breast-feeding contributing to intelligence use social and genetic factors to explain these IQ differences. (Mothers who breast-feed score, on average, much higher on IQ tests than those who bottle-feed, indicating that genetic factors play an important role.)

How though, does our early life affect our later intellectual performance? Studies have shown that children whose mothers were thirty-five or older at the time of their birth score approximately 6 IQ points higher than those whose mothers were twenty or younger.[11] Further investigations suggest that children who used a dummy score 3–5 points lower than those who did not, and that children whose fathers were in non-manual jobs at the time of birth score significantly higher than those with a manual worker as a father. Another general rule thought to be applicable is that the more older brothers and sisters a child has, the lower their IQ will be.[12]

Judging from the huge number of studies conducted in this field, we could make endless statements about an individual's expected IQ score, based on all sorts of obscure theories, but would this be fair? Perhaps, before we point the finger at those we expect to do less well intellectually, we should remind ourselves of an important point made in Chapter 5. Just because a child fits into all the categories thought to adversely affect intelligence, they do not have to have very low intelligence. All we know is that they are more likely to score lower on an IQ test, which is not necessarily the same thing.

A Question of Class

Social class also appears to be inextricably linked with what we perceive to be intelligence. Maybe your income does affect how intelligent your child can become. Does coming from a 'better class' enable you to get a better job? If so, you may wonder whether it's due to your inherent intelligence or your family background. There are numerous related questions, such as, is a public school education better than a comprehensive education? Or, does the sound of an upper-class accent give an impression of being more intelligent?

Nowadays the class system, even in the UK, is more fluid than it once was. It is now based more on intelligence and the movement through society that this allows. Let us look at how this works. Parents from any background will probably have children of the same intelligence or slightly different from themselves, whether higher or lower. Those with higher intelligence are likely to get better jobs, with better pay and therefore rise up the social hierarchy. Meanwhile, those with lower intelligence will probably get not-so-good jobs with less pay, and fall in the social order. Those with the same intelligence, meanwhile, will most likely remain in the class they were born to. (This theory only, of course, applies on average; there is no accounting for particular individuals.)

Occupational Status

In real life there are usually very slight differences between the occupational status of members of the same family. In most cases relatives also have occupations with very similar, if not identical, status – the closer the relationship, the more similar the occupational status. The immediate conclusion, both obvious and controversial, is that just as intelligence tends to run in families, both from a genetic and environmental point of view, status (including occupational status) will also run in families, shifting only slightly from generation to generation.

One study, from Denmark, looked at exactly this phenomenon, considering over 100 men and women adopted in and around Copenhagen between 1924 and 1947.[13] All the adoptees considered in this study had little in common with their biological siblings, but, of course, did share a common environment with their adoptive siblings. It was found that, while biologically related siblings closely resembled each other in terms of occupational status, adoptive siblings did not significantly correlate with each other. Other results showed that full siblings had occupations which were much more closely aligned than half siblings.

ABNORMAL UPBRINGING

One area which appears to be well worth investigating is that of children who have, for one reason or another, been raised in abnormal, even non-human, situations. When returned to society, can such children learn about things they have not previously witnessed? What level of IQ can they achieve?

One case is that of monozygotic twin boys who were discovered in the part of Czechoslovakia that is now the Czech Republic in the autumn of 1967.[14] Their mother had died giving birth to them, and after spending eighteen months in and out of children's homes they went to live with their father, stepmother, two elder sisters and two children of their stepmother, in a small town suburb, where no one knew the family. When the boys were discovered five and a half years later it was found that they had suffered abnormally deprived conditions, under a psychopathic stepmother and a weak-willed father.

The boys had been forced to live in a small unheated closet in which they were often locked, sleeping on a polythene sheet. They received only hostility from all members of the family, at the instigation of their stepmother: they were regularly beaten, and could not talk or play with the other children. They were seldom let out of the closet and were never allowed outside, growing up in almost total isolation with inadequate food, light and even fresh air.

When discovered the boys could barely walk, and when given shoes could not walk at all. They were completely scared and mistrustful of mechanical toys, TV, ordinary street traffic and so on. They communicated with each other mostly in sign language, being able to only poorly imitate two or three words of adult speech at a time. The boys' play was at first very primitive, but as they became familiar with toys and their surroundings it rapidly improved, although joining in with other children remained a problem. One major surprise was that the boys could not understand the meaning of pictures.

From late 1968 to mid-1969 the boys were observed closely in a children's home and some progress was seen. In July 1969, however, the twins went to live with a new foster family where they were made to feel very happy. In the fifteen months to September 1969 their mental age increased by three years, a remarkable achievement. At that time they entered the first class of a school for retarded children but soon excelled in this environment and subsequently entered a normal school.

It was felt that they were, by that time, only about three years behind the usual educational pace. A few years later they were average for their age range. A major factor in their ability to get over their abysmal early situation was thought to be the fact that, as twins, they could share the problem with each other in a way that a single child could not have done.

Other examples of severe deprivation concern single children and have had very different results. One twelve-year-old boy, called Peter, was discovered, in 1724, near Hameln in Germany.[15] When found he made no human sounds, and sat on all fours. He preferred raw vegetables and grass to cooked foods, and ate pieces of birds that he had captured and dismembered. His sense of smell was reported to be sharp and he seemed to have learnt for himself how to survive in a forest. It appeared that he had not been raised by humans. An attempt was made to teach him to speak, but this failed.

Another boy, named Victor, was discovered in 1799, living under roughly similar circumstances to Peter, in Caure Woods, France.[16] On discovery Victor was taken to Paris and paraded as a circus attraction. He spent most of his time rocking backwards and forwards like an animal in a zoo, a man-animal only interested in eating and sleeping. Victor appeared not even to perceive that certain sounds were produced by humans, let alone that they could have some meaning. Again little progress was achieved in attempting to educate him.

One further case appeared in the early 1900s, when two girls, Kamala and Amala, were discovered living with three adult wolves and two cubs.[17] Their human instincts appeared to be dormant and animal instincts had taken over. Amala soon died but Kamala lived with a family and was studied at length. She ate only with her mouth, not using her hands, and would frequently become ill from over-eating. She enjoyed raw meat and was not toilet-trained. She was lacking in many human traits such as sorrow, or a sense of humour, and had very little curiosity. Although reasonable intellectual and emotional progress was made (for example she achieved a vocabulary of thirty words and showed some limited signs of affection), she died at the age of seventeen, about nine years after her discovery.

In the cases of the boy twins and the wolf children, where there was early human contact (with each other) but the children went through a period of deprivation, it was possible to retrieve the situation and carry out some learning at a later stage. For Peter and Victor, however, who apparently had experienced no human contact, even with another child, it did not seem possible to pull them out of their 'wild animal' type ways. They had learnt to behave differently and that was that.

It seems that certain mental functions are learnt at particular ages, the period just before and after birth being perhaps the most critical because the rate of brain cell connections being made appears to be highest at that time. As a child gets older, so they learn and adapt less and less. For children who have been completely and utterly deprived of specific pointers to aid their learning at these crucial times, it can be too late to pick up the pieces later on. However, in the case of children who are deprived together as a pair some limited mutual learning can still go on. This small, but important basis, can later enable children to progress much faster.

The issues raised by these studies are very complex. But, essentially, it would appear that if we can change factors in the lives of a whole group of people we will in so doing be able to raise their average IQ. The deprived children studies show that the group whose IQ we wish to improve must have had a variety of exposures, before our intervention. As long as they have experienced some positive human interaction at some point then we have a chance. If not, then that aspect of their lives, whatever it is, may be lacking forever. Quite simply, the sooner in a child's life that any intervention can occur, the more malleable they are and the more chance there is of improving their abilities in certain ways.

RACE

The most controversial area in the study of human intelligence is that of race – so much so that books on the subject which have drawn unfashionable conclusions have been banned or even destroyed.

The aims of research have shifted strongly first in one direction and then in the other. For example, it has been observed that black children tend to do less well on IQ tests than white children. This 'fact' has subsequently been used to excuse racist behaviour, ill treatment, slavery, sterilisation and even murder. But what about the role of environmental and genetic factors in determining an individual's IQ test performance?

If the balance of intelligence is, as many suggest, roughly 60 per cent genetic and 40 per cent environmental then the larger, genetic percentage provides a pattern of continuation. Indeed, to take an extreme case, if intelligence was 100 per cent genetically inherited and no interracial marriages took place, we would have, without question, races with different standards of intelligence. In this sense, a group of individuals, a race, going from generation to generation on an isolated island, even with the 60/40 split, will have its own average intelligence associated with it.

In 1972 Charles Lindbergh discovered a primitive cave-dwelling tribe, called the Tasaday, in a Philippine rainforest. They wore loin cloths and lived on a jungle cliff edge. There had been 'No sign of any attempt to improve or modify their caves in any way although generation after generation apparently had lived in them.'[18] Their intelligence was clearly associated with their own, primitive way of life.

A further point to remember, as we have seen, is that intelligence is subjective. If, let us say, a white American male has set a series of questions to test intelligence then these questions will probably be best suited to other white American males. They will most likely not favour black American females, Russians, Indians or even white Canadian males. So when it is stated, for example, that black children tended to do less well on an IQ test than white children, we must be clear about the test conditions and in particular who set the test.

Interestingly, it is East Asians (such as Chinese and Japanese) who generally do best on IQ tests, whether they be resident in Asia, America or Europe. This could have some link with their high fish diet, or conversely it could be linked to the relative values placed on different subjects. In these countries mathematics and science are seen as important elements in the education of all children. Meanwhile in the USA, and Western Europe in particular, literature takes a more central position and many children can 'opt out' of science at an early age. Not surprisingly, therefore, East Asians tend to score higher on non-verbal tests, whilst not doing so well on verbal tests.

Many studies have been carried out in the USA comparing white Americans (generally of North European origin) with black Americans (generally of African origin). Over the past few decades the difference in average scores – blacks compared to whites – has narrowed by only about 3 IQ points.[19] This is due, it is felt, to a smaller number of very low scores amongst the black community, rather than a shift elsewhere. Economic improvements, better public health and diminishing racism in the USA all help to support this argument. At present, however, an average white American achieves higher IQ test scores than 84 per cent of blacks, whilst an average black person achieves higher scores than 16 per cent of whites.[20] Average performances are therefore still significantly different. These figures relate to a mean IQ value for whites of 100, compared to 85 for blacks.

As one might expect, great efforts have been taken to remove obvious, present-day cultural biases from the test procedure. One example is the 'Digit Span' sub-test, in which the subject has to try to repeat a sequence of numbers in the order originally given. The subject then has to repeat the same sequence but in reverse order, which is more of a mental challenge. In most studies, the difference in results between blacks and whites is about twice as great (i.e. blacks do relatively worse on the reversal digits than on the forward digits). Reasons involving lack of motivation or willingness to do the tests, which could be used to explain the differences between black and white scores in general, seem to fall down when results of this type are obtained.[21]

If we look at the physical make-up of blacks as compared to whites there are clear differences, not only in colour. In many power or speed sports black competitors tend to fare better than whites. No one suggests there is anything wrong with these differences existing. Each individual does what they can do physically, and in certain tests (such as running fast over 100 metres) it may be a black person who wins. Certainly there does not appear to be a drive to attempt to prove that there are, on average, no physical differences between blacks and whites.

Just as there may be physical differences between blacks and whites, so there may be mental differences. There is nothing wrong with this; indeed all differences can be seen in a positive light. On any mental test blacks and whites will, on average, perform differently, depending on who is best suited to that particular test. But the results from such tests merely show who did best on that test. IQ tests only focus on certain aspects of intelligence; they certainly do not give a complete picture. So we must be careful about what conclusions we actually draw from test results, particularly when comparing races. Where there are differences, however, we should not ignore them because of moral considerations. Throughout history the progress of science has been impeded by results being viewed in a strange way due to religion or moral standpoint. Surely we must have learnt by now to look at results objectively and not to insert unnecessary bias in our analysis of them.

Some tests have looked at Reaction Time (RT) and Movement Time (MT) in an attempt to find a link between physical and mental powers. Subjects are given a very simple cognitive test and precise timing is used to see how fast they carry out each element. Consistent results have been obtained to show that white people are fastest on RT, but black people are fastest on MT. It is felt by some,[22] that RT relates closely to IQ-type tests – in fact they identify it with the 'g' factor in the Two-Factor Theory of Spearman.

At this point bias starts to creep in, under the guise of a 'sound' philosophical argument, which goes as follows: We all have a general mental ability, 'g'. If RT is linked with 'g' then those who do better on RT must have a better 'g' than those who do worse. But this is by no means a logical conclusion. RT represents, at most, just one aspect of 'g'; a faster/better RT merely indicates a different 'g' from another individual. The only way we could conclude, from this evidence, that an individual's 'g' was also better would be if we had conclusive evidence of such links, which we don't have!

Intelligence and social and economic status are clearly part of a feedback loop: an individual's intelligence will influence their social and economic status, as will the environment in which they are born and grow up. Such factors will then strongly influence that individual's offspring, who may themselves rise or fall in social and economic status, depending on their own intelligence. There is therefore a certain amount of change, but a considerable amount of behaviour is due to the circumstances in which individuals find themselves. Such circumstances are certain to manifest, on average, on a racial basis.

It has been found that, on average, black Africans obtain substantially lower IQ test scores than black Americans. This is not at all surprising, due to the cultural differences, test learning and ongoing Americanisation of the latter group, with their different, more technically oriented, environment. However, it does indicate the shift in performance obtainable en masse, as a group evolves in a new environment.

Within a particular environment, as different groups evolve together, so differences between them will remain in the short term, but will gradually diminish in the long term. Where groups evolve in distinctly different environments so differences between them may appear roughly static in the short term but will, again, gradually diverge in the long term. In this way black Americans will diverge, in IQ performance, from black Africans whilst converging with white Americans.

In short-term tests, despite a general upward shift in IQ performance for the population as a whole, the relative standing of ethnic groups has remained almost the same, showing a slight tendency to converge. Where mixed race marriages occur, so convergence of the population as a whole is obviously more rapid; although the immediate social positioning of mixed-race children is a rather complex issue, with such individuals not necessarily fitting in easily to any particular racial grouping.

A major element of much white-oriented research used to be the desire to find scientific reasoning to conclude that white people were somehow 'better' than black people, as opposed to 'different'. One example of this was the research carried out by Etienne Serres in 1860. He observed that the distance between the navel and the penis in a male baby is small, relative to body height. In white adults the ratio is greater, less so in yellows, and in black adults never much more than babies. Serres' conclusion was that black people remain perpetually like children, in terms of their intelligence![23]

S. G. Morton, one of the great nineteenth-century American scientists, when linking brain size with intelligence, collected over 1000 skulls. His hard data was reported to show the superiority of whites over blacks, and – among whites – that Anglo-Saxons were above Jews. There have been claims, however, that Morton 'unconsciously' doctored his results in order to reach the conclusions he wanted.[24] (Other researchers disagree with this and have produced evidence to back up Morton's results and conclusions.)[25]

Quite clearly, on mental tests, such as IQ tests, blacks and whites perform differently. This is mainly likely to be due to inherited characteristics. If those black and white people live in the same environment then, very, very gradually the differences will probably diminish. While we should not ignore or cover up these differences, we should be careful about saying that whites are better than blacks, or indeed vice versa, unless we clearly state the tests on which that statement is based. As the results of any tests are, at best, only loosely connected with intelligence, we must also be very careful about claiming that one race is, on average, more intelligent than another.

WHAT REALLY MAKES A DIFFERENCE?

In looking at how all these factors affect intelligence in humans, we have had to resort to IQ test results as the only available yardstick, even though, as we saw in Chapter 5, they are very poor indicators of general intelligence. Unfortunately there is at present very little else from which we can draw scientific data as to what is good or bad in terms of our intelligence. There are evidential results linking different foods with IQ test performance, and it is the same story with different classes, races and even different sexes. Where there are physical differences it follows that there are likely to be mental differences.

It would appear that the intelligence in different races is itself different; the intelligence in different classes is itself different; and the intelligence in different sexes is itself different. Importantly, it is only considered in terms of 'better' or 'worse' when a subjective measure is applied.

Genetic inheritance clearly plays a role in our intelligence. Indeed this appears to be true in all beings. With humans, it is also possible to manipulate an individual's intelligence by adjusting their environment; whilst factors such as pollution appear to play only a limited role, nutrition seems to have a major input. A balanced diet is important, as we saw earlier in this chapter, and a regular intake of vitamin C supplement can, it appears, have a long-term positive effect, certainly in terms of IQ test results and thereby potentially in examinations.

Most studies have looked into the long-term effects of an individual's environment on his or her intelligence. But short-term effects are also important. For instance, if you want to be at your intellectual best, possibly for an exam, in half an hour's time, then what should you do – read a book and drink orange juice, or go for a walk and eat chocolate? In the next chapter I will report on the results of an extensive study looking into just this question. I guarantee the results will startle you.

7
How to Improve
Your IQ
Test Results

THE FACT THAT THERE IS A STRONG genetic influence on an
individual's intelligence is all well and good. But, once you are
born, you are stuck with what you have. And when it comes to many
of the environmental effects on intelligence, knowledge of them comes
rather late. It is not possible to tell your eighteen-year-old mother not
to give birth to you for another fifteen years, for example. Nor is it
really possible to tell her not to keep putting that dummy in your
mouth. So is it all too late? Is there anything you personally can do
to improve your intelligence?

Let's say you have an hour or so to go before a vitally important
examination. Can you do anything right now to maximise your
chances of success, or has your result already been determined by
long-term genetic or environmental factors? In order to get a good
idea of what might be possible, a series of experiments was designed
specifically for this book.

The experiments were carried out in October 1999 and involved 120 students from the University of Reading. The vast majority of these were First Year students (Freshers) from a variety of courses, and all took part voluntarily in the exercise. Although both male and female students were involved, no attempt was otherwise made to obtain a representative cross-section of the population.

The experiment was designed to look at the response of a number of students, all of whom were very familiar with studying and taking examinations.

The students were asked a series of questions of an IQ test type. Two examples of the questions actually asked are as follows:

a. Insert the word that means the same as the two words outside the brackets:

Stake(. . . .)mail

b. Insert the missing number:

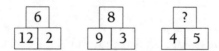

The answers for these are a. post; and b. 11. In b. there are various sequences, but each set of three numbers adds up to 20. Other questions involved spatial awareness, anagrams and sequencing.

During the experiment the students were required to sit one IQ test, carry out an activity and/or partake of refreshments, and then take a further IQ test. In each case the actual IQ score of any individual was not of particular interest. Rather, the change in IQ score (depending on the exercise or refreshment taken) was the critical factor. Essentially, the results show the difference in IQ results that can be obtained if a particular exercise or refreshment is taken in the half hour before the test.

Although no direct claim can be made as to the effect on one's intelligence of taking the particular exercise or refreshment, IQ test results do appear to relate to examination performance. We can therefore deduce, from the results obtained, what is the best policy for a student in the time available. The results obtained were, as you will see, extremely surprising.

Ten activities were investigated, as follows:

A – Playing with a construction toy
B – Doing the *Times* crossword
C – Going for a walk
D – Sitting, chatting
E – Watching *This Morning* on TV
F – Watching a TV documentary
G – Watching *Friends* on TV
H – Listening to classical music
I – Reading a book
J – Meditation

To expand on some of these: the TV programme *This Morning* is a TV chat show hosted by Richard Madeley and Judy Finnigan; the TV documentary shown was a rather technically oriented BBC film entitled *Digital Planet*; *Friends* is the TV situation comedy from the USA; the classical music being played was Vivaldi's *Four Seasons*.

The results obtained were normalised such that the average IQ score on each test was held to be 120. This was so that the relative increase or decrease in IQ score could be measured in relation to the activity carried out. The overall ease, or otherwise, of a particular test was not of interest.

In Table 7.1 the relative performance in IQ results achieved when undertaking each activity is shown, with 1 being the best, and 10 the worst.

The results shown are absolutely astonishing. The overall winner,

Table 7.1: Activities ranked by their effect on IQ score

Activity	Males	Females	Overall
Construction toy	10	9	9
Crossword	7	2	6
Walking	4	6	5
Chatting	6	8	7
This Morning	2	1	1
Documentary	1	5	2
Friends	5	3	4
Classical music	8	7	8
Book	9	10	10
Meditation	3	4	3

proving a good activity with both males and females, is watching a TV chat show, although for males watching a TV documentary was in fact the better option. All three TV choices came in the top four of the overall results, with meditation sneaking in to upset a clean sweep. There can be no question though – watching TV immediately before a test is the best way to improve your IQ and examination performance.

In most cases the results showed considerable consistency between males and females. Meditation seemed to work reasonably well for both males and females, while listening to classical music did not seem to be too useful. The two clear worst categories were playing with the construction toy and reading a book, both requiring concentration and thought (the book selected was *March of the Machines*). The only slightly inconsistent result appears to be doing *The Times* crossword, which appears to have had a much better effect on females than males.

When we look at the IQ score differences, however, as shown in Graph 7.1, 7.2 and 7.3, we can see that females were certainly much more affected by the activity carried out than the males. As changes of more than plus or minus 3 in IQ score are considered significant, the results obtained here are of major importance (where no bar appears, no change occurred).

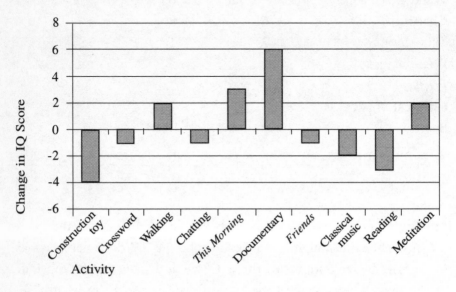

Graph 7.1: Changes in male IQ score due to activity

The results within these graphs have been scaled in order to give an average of zero change. So the closer a score is to zero, the nearer that activity is to having no effect. The more positive the score, the more that activity helps the IQ score, and so on. The scores have been taken to the nearest integer.

To summarise the results from Table 7.1 and Graphs 7.1, 7.2 and 7.3, it would appear best for a male student to either watch a technical documentary or a TV chat show, while avoiding playing with a construction toy or reading a book. For females, meanwhile, reading a book is definitely a no-no, as is the construction toy. Watching a

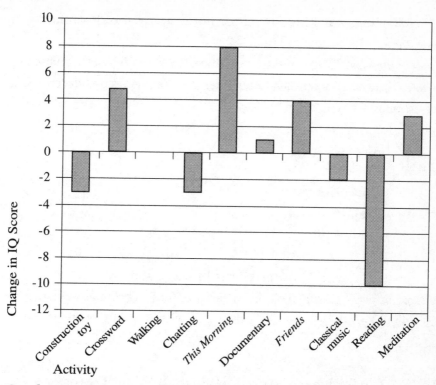

Graph 7.2: Changes in female IQ score due to activity

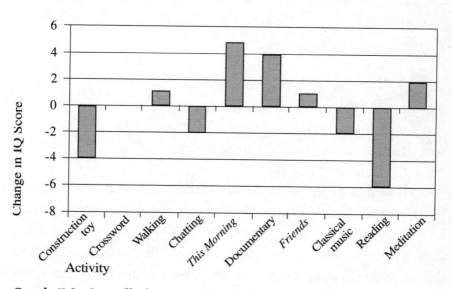

Graph 7.3: Overall change in IQ score due to activity

TV chat show, watching *Friends* or doing a crossword would, how-ever, appear to be useful aids.

As well as different activities, the effects on IQ performance of taking different types of refreshment were also considered. The refreshments were:

A – Alcohol (beer)
B – Coffee
C – Chocolate (bar)
D – Peanuts (salted)
E – Orange juice

In the results given, the effects of sugar and milk in the coffee, where this was taken, have been factored out. The relative perform-ance in IQ tests is given in Table 7.2, with 1 again being the best position.

Table 7.2: refreshments ranked by their effect on IQ score

Refreshment	Males	Females	Overall
Beer	3	3	3
Coffee	1	1	1
Chocolate	5	4	4
Peanuts	2	2	2
Juice	4	5	5

Coffee had a fairly uniform positive effect on IQ results, as did, to a lesser extent, eating peanuts. Results were, in this respect, similar between males and females. Conversely, and quite surprisingly, orange juice had uniformly the opposite, negative effect. While vitamin C seems to have a good long-term effect on IQ, its short-term effect appears to be rather negative. Chocolate also did not do well in the test, particularly amongst males.

Perhaps the most surprising result of all was the fact that alcohol gave very mixed results. In fact the response to alcohol varied far more than any other. For some students it had a remarkably positive effect, whereas for others its effect was just as remarkably negative. Overall, however, it averaged out as mid-ranking, although this is deceptive. Perhaps the message should be, if you are aware that alcohol can have a stimulating effect then consider partaking; otherwise steer clear! This said, one of the most strikingly positive results on IQ for both males and females, was the combined effect of alcohol and watching a TV chat show!

In graphs 7.4, 7.5 and 7.6 we can see the scaled results of the different refreshments on IQ scores.

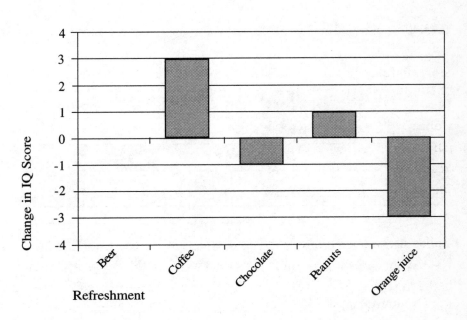

Graph 7.4: Changes in male IQ scores due to refreshment

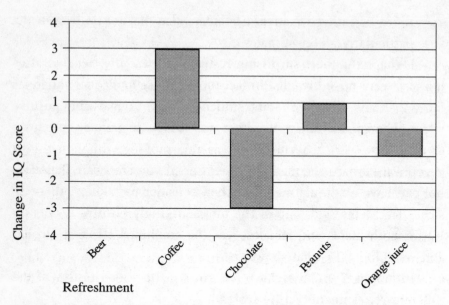

Graph 7.5: Changes in female IQ score due to refreshment

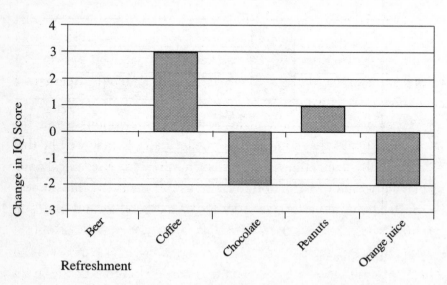

Graph 7.6: Overall changes in IQ score due to refreshment

The conclusion from these results must be that if you have half an hour to go before an examination then it is well worth having a cup of coffee and perhaps eating peanuts. In particular, the 3-point increase on IQ score obtained from coffee appeared to be a fairly consistent result amongst all those taking part in the experiment.

While the refreshment results were steadier and reasonably predictable, the activity results were extremely surprising. Sitting and talking to friends, which is probably what quite a few people do before an examination, turns out to be perhaps not such a good idea. As with other activities, results were pretty uniform between men and women. The construction toy, walking, chatting, listening to music and meditation all produced similar results for men and women, while watching *Friends* appeared to have a reasonably positive effect for women and a slightly negative one for men.

It may be that the technical nature of the documentary watched and the book read had a detrimental effect on the female results. If both had been less technically oriented then perhaps the male and female results would have been similar here too. With the TV chat show having slightly more of an effect on women than men, the difference in crossword results is difficult to explain. Nevertheless, linking the results together, we can conclude that a good strategy directly before an examination is to drink coffee and watch TV (perhaps a chat show or documentary).

These results overturn many common assumptions about the kinds of activities that stimulate us intellectually. It may well be that more mentally demanding activities, such as reading a technical book or playing with a construction toy, tire us out mentally, thus impeding our short-term performance. Whilst being good for our brains in the long term, they are not so good as far as our immediate output is concerned. An analogy can be drawn, in a physical sense, with an athlete who benefits from a relaxing warm-up routine before a big race but does not exhaust himself by running several miles before the event. It certainly indicates that last-minute swatting before an exam is not such a good idea.

One thing is clear, and that is that some significant differences in IQ scores were obtained in response to certain activities and refreshments. If IQ results bear any relationship to intelligence at all then this means that the experience of an individual immediately prior to a point in time can have a profound effect on their intelligence at that point in time.

We have already seen that intelligence is subjective, and hence tests, such as the IQ tests used in this experiment, tend to be subjective to those within a given class, sex or race. In our experiment, however, we were not so concerned with actual test results for an individual, whether poor or excellent. Rather, we were interested in how much an individual could themselves change their result by a selected course of action.

Some people, however, push our understanding of intelligence to the limit. When individuals are so far from the norm it can be difficult to know what intelligence means. Is a genius super-intelligent because they can do one thing very well? And what about someone who suffers from a mental disability? Let us look next at how human intelligence can be stretched in different directions.

8

INTELLIGENCE
OUT OF
BALANCE

ALTHOUGH NO ONE IS COMPLETELY normal (we all have our foibles), in some cases the abnormalities exceed commonly accepted limits. This can mean that individuals cannot perform adequately mentally in one or a number of ways or that their performance is phenomenal in one or a number of ways, or indeed both of these. In order to get a better general understanding of human intelligence we need to explore what being a genius actually means and we shall also take a look at mental functioning deemed to be abnormal.

MENTAL GIFTS

Some individuals clearly have extraordinary natural talents or abilities. Such individuals, particularly when children, are commonly labelled 'geniuses'. What effect does this sort of label have on a child? And why are there geniuses in the first place?

No matter how or why an individual becomes classified as a genius the effects are dramatic. There have been cases of children aged ten to twelve winning university places by doing extremely well in examinations normally taken by seventeen- or eighteen-year-olds. A child aged ten is by and large still aged ten mentally in most aspects of life, even if they are able to perform very well in one or two specific examinations. University life, however, is geared towards those who are much older. It is not purely an environment of study. Instead it is one where mature individuals also learn important life skills.

Should young children really be placed in a university environment? Will they not miss out on the developmental experiences normally associated with childhood? Such experiences help to form the personality of an individual and allow them to interact better with others in their own age group.

The question of how and why genius arises in particular individuals is closely related to the nature versus nurture argument (discussed in Chapter 4). One famous example is Wolfgang Amadeus Mozart, who was a capable pianist and composer by an extremely young age. He was gifted with musical abilities at birth, but his subsequent achievements were realised following thousands of hours of practice. Mozart's father, Leopold, was a hard taskmaster who rarely allowed his son to venture outside, or to play with friends. Instead Mozart had to spend his every waking hour on music practice. From the time he was six years old he was travelling around Europe, playing at palaces and other venues in order to make money.

It cannot be denied that Mozart was an extremely talented individual, but the extent to which he was pushed by his father must have had some effect on the way his genius was expressed. Perhaps, as Edison suggested, 'genius is 1 per cent inspiration and 99 per cent perspiration'. Mozart, like others, needed a long period of learning before he reached the peak of his profession. The same appears to be true of all creative artists. While a proportion of genius can be put down to innate, genetic characteristics, hard work also plays a vital part.

Occasionally a child will be hailed as a prodigy simply because they can achieve tasks well beyond the capabilities of most adults. George Biddler was such a child. Born in 1806, he became interested in mental arithmetic at an early age. By nine years old, although unable to read or write, he was being paraded at fairs up and down the UK to show off his ability to solve mathematical problems, and had acquired the nickname 'the calculating boy'. He entered Edinburgh University at the age of fourteen where he made friends with Robert Stephenson, the son of George the railway engineer. As a result, he had a remarkably successful career as a railway engineer designing railways, docks (including London Victoria docks), bridges, ships and telegraph works.[1]

Another child prodigy was Norbert Weiner. Born in 1894, Weiner actually became the founder of modern cybernetics. Like Mozart, Norbert had an extremely demanding father. A professor at Harvard University, Weiner Senior took charge of his son's education from the age of seven, employing Harvard students to teach him subjects such as chemistry and Latin. Norbert began a degree course at Tufts University at the age of eleven, which he had successfully completed by fourteen. He followed this with a PhD at Harvard, which he obtained at eighteen. By the age of twenty-five he had gained a post at the Massachusetts Institute of Technology where he remained as a world-renowned mathematician for thirty-three years. Despite his vast intellectual success Norbert Weiner is reported to have been very unhappy. Although far advanced in academic subjects he had few social abilities and was unable to lead a normal life.[2]

What do these examples of child prodigies tell us about

intelligence? An important factor would seem to be the desires and aspirations of the parents. The parents of such children are usually well-educated themselves, and have a high level of concern about their children's education, often making considerable efforts to provide them with the best possible opportunities. Both nature and nurture clearly play important parts in forming a child genius. Without a spark of inborn talent all the pushing in the world will not result in extra-ordinary intellectual development. On the other hand, without encouragement in childhood, the individual's brilliance may not be revealed until later on, or may never develop at all. Charles Darwin, for example, was not an exceptional child. Neither was Albert Einstein, although both were brought up in intellectual homes.

Child prodigies, also known in recent years as 'gifted' children, are well aware of what is expected of them; they know that failure will be greeted with disapproval. Often social interaction with children of the same age is highly restricted, and their enforced interests usually differ from those of the majority of children (for example, nowadays they may not be allowed to watch television). Also, because of their advanced intellectual performance, they are placed in classes where everyone else is considerably older.

In recent years more and more children have been diagnosed as 'gifted'. In October 1998 Isknader Yusof, aged eleven, and his sister Aisha, sixteen, made academic history when they began university careers at Warwick.

Another of their siblings, Sufiah, commenced a course in mathematics at Oxford University a year earlier, then aged thirteen; while their four-year-old sister Zuleika is expected to sit her maths A-level by the age of six. All these children were largely educated at home. Their father, Farooq Yusof, described his role as that of 'a committed parent', but denied that his children had been 'hot housed'.

The Yusof children have followed in the footsteps of Ruth Lawrence who got a First Class Honours degree from Oxford in mathematics, at the age of thirteen. Although she went on to obtain an overseas academic appointment, at the time Ruth's father was criticised for chaperoning her too intently.

In February 2000 all these children were thoroughly eclipsed by Justin Chapman who embarked on a course at the University of Rochester, New York at the age of six, taking ancient history. Justin was again taught at home, from the age of two, when his mother first noticed his reading abilities. In fact she has had to accompany him at university, because the doors are too heavy for him to open on his own.

But how far are these 'exceptional' abilities simply due to 'fast-track' individual lessons? Do such children often have mental break-downs and fail to cope with life in general, particularly as they get older?

Research has shown that child prodigies rarely 'burn out'.[3] Most of them tend to carry their abilities through to later life, although they are usually apparent in only one subject area. Other skills present in these individuals may be perfectly normal, better or worse than those of 'unexceptional' people.

Many people believe that those who achieve fame, such as film stars, or those labelled as geniuses, are distinctly different from every-one else. They are popularly assumed to produce their works of genius without any effort. And this idea has taken hold to such an extent that virtually everything these individuals do is believed to be extraordinarily brilliant.

In truth, whether it be a book, a painting or a musical composition, the completion of a masterpiece requires a considerable amount of conscious effort. Furthermore, a genius will not always produce outstanding work; they are more than likely to produce some bad or at least pretty ordinary results.

Whether or not an individual is classified as a genius, particularly in the arts, partly depends on the ideals and values of the time.

The world must be ready for the talents of the person in question: too radical and they could be dismissed as crazy; not radical enough and they may not attract attention. Like intelligence as a whole, genius is to some extent subjective. What might be seen as genius by one person may not be by another. And any act of genius must be accepted and recognised by the society in which it occurs.

MENTAL DISABILITIES

Evolution in humans tends to stretch capabilities, both physically and mentally. Parents who themselves have brains which push mental capabilities in one direction may well produce children who stretch these capabilities even further. While such individuals can otherwise still function normally, because of their exceptional skills they may be classed as geniuses. However, if, through evolution, things go too far, they effectively become too good. The boundary of normal behaviour is then breached, and the individual may be labelled 'mentally sub-normal', 'retarded' or even insane. As has often been observed, the line between genius and insanity is a thin one.

A wide variety of people function mentally in a way that is considered to be outside the normal boundaries, and some of them are classified as mentally disabled. But how do such people fit with our concept of intelligence? Whilst some mental disorders appear to affect many aspects of intelligence others may only relate to a very limited range of mental skills. Of all mental disorders, autism is perhaps the most interesting, due to its extremely diverse manifestations. For this reason, I have chosen to place particular emphasis on autism when discussing mental disorders and intelligence.

The term autism in fact covers a wide range of conditions affecting both mental and physical performance, including severe social interaction problems, severe communication problems, lack of imaginative activity, and a restricted repertoire of activities and interests.

In many cases these attributes go hand in hand with other features such as mental retardation, unusual postures, strange motor behaviours (such as arms flapping wildly), ignoring pain, over-reaction to sound, abnormalities in drinking, sleeping and mood, and even self-injury.

Autistic children are easily distracted even by the most minor things. They are very selective about which stimuli they respond to, paying no attention at all to those they have no interest in. This is coupled with a lack of desire for learning (including the exploration of new toys or objects). They would rather carry out highly repetitive, isolated actions without involving anything novel or complex. This means that autistic people often have severe problems with language development.

In the words of Jarred Blackburn, himself autistic:

I like people, but I find them most strange, illogical, petty and superficial. I can intellectually grasp, but not relate to the motives. Common gender roles seem totally illogical to me: my concept of male and female is purely anatomical . . . With people I know well, I may not say much, because I have run out of things to tell them . . . I may forget even the most basic vocabulary words like knife, restaurant, or even my own name . . . I cannot scan words directly into meaning, I must process letter by letter, syllable by syllable, so it takes me a long time to read . . . I might ask a question about one subject and get an answer about another totally unrelated subject . . . people have a tendency to read emotional context into things I say, when none is intended: to me 'I am unhappy' is a fact, it is all just information to be transmitted . . . I am bothered by certain noises . . . I have trouble processing many things at once . . . when people try to get my attention they slow me down and annoy me.[4]

What causes autism? This is not an easy question to answer. Autism is an extremely complex disorder, so much so that it is yet to be fully explained. Genetic factors – nature – are certainly felt to play a part, although complications in pregnancy also seem to have a role in some cases. Research shows that the majority of autistic children have at least one parent who has been classified as highly intelligent, and who has more eccentricities than is usual.[5] The environment – nurture – is not thought to play such an important part, but it is quite possible that influences in the formative years may have a significant effect. As with the classification of genius, the truth is probably that both genetics and environment contribute to autism.

An intriguing aspect of autism is that of the *autistic savant*. An *autistic savant* is a person with very low IQ test scores, who nevertheless displays exceptional skills and abilities in certain areas. A famous example of this phenomenon was portrayed by Dustin Hoffman in the film *Rainman*. The character he played was autistic but exhibited tremendous feats of memory, and mathematical abilities well beyond those of a normal person.

It is estimated that about 10 per cent of autistic people are *savants* – each with different abilities. The most common trait amongst this group is an obsession with a very narrow task or subject area. In a sense these people appear to be capable of massively 'over-learning' in one particular area. Perhaps more autistic people are *savants* but they may not have had an opportunity to prove their abilities, possibly because their skills are difficult or impossible to demonstrate.

Two examples of acknowledged *savants* are Stephen and Christopher. Stephen is autistic but has incredible artistic talent. He can stand before an object or scene for about fifteen minutes and later confidently draw exactly what he has seen from memory. His drawings have uncanny depth and accuracy. Stephen prefers to draw buildings, possibly because of their structure, and he likes the scene to be complicated. Perhaps one of the most interesting features of his draw-ings is that they are an exact mirror image of the scenes themselves.

Christopher, meanwhile, has been institutionalised from his birth in 1962. He cannot reliably find his way around, has very poor co-ordination and fails to understand numbers. From the age of three, however, he has had an interest in factual books, particularly those dealing with languages. He can read, write and communicate fluent-ly in twenty languages from a wide range of cultures. He can also follow different scripts e.g. Greek, Cyrillic (Russian) and Devanagari (Hindi). In 1992 he was given two days to prepare himself for a Dutch TV programme which he duly appeared on communicating entirely in Dutch, learnt from a basic grammar book and a dictionary.[6]

DIFFERENT ASPECTS OF INTELLIGENCE

Clearly people with autism and other mental disabilities, such as senil-ity, are thinking in a different way from most of us. Their intelligence is outside the bounds associated with normal behaviour. As such, they make us question our definitions of intelligence when it comes to tak-ing measurements and comparing one person with another. For example, if an intelligence test involves memorising random numbers, a number of people with autism are likely to do very well – proba-bly better than those of so-called normal intelligence.

In recent years, academic institutions have begun to make allowances for certain mental conditions. For example, individuals with dyslexia have problems understanding written text and/or com-posing written text – the ordering of letters can be extremely diffi-cult. Now most universities and schools allow more time in examinations for such students, in an attempt to help their situation relative to other students. Whilst this is felt to be morally laudible, it really means that we are trying to exempt certain mental functions from being considered as factors in intelligence. Should we, for example, also allow extra marks or time for students with a poor memory, or those who cannot deal with numbers? Where do we draw the line?

It appears that an individual's brain is structured in a certain way, working more easily in certain aspects of intelligence than others. The full extent of capabilities can be realised by environmental stimuli, including training. Where abilities are particularly good in one direction, and there is sufficient commitment, a person may be hailed as a genius. However, this has little or nothing to do with their intelligence in other aspects. Other individuals may have a brain structure, possibly coupled with environmental effects, that results in capabilities that are so good in one direction that their brain cannot function normally in other ways. These individuals may be classified as subnormal beings unable to function in some aspects of normal life.

Intelligence, it seems, has many different aspects. Extraordinary performance in any particular aspect can lead to an individual being labelled as eccentric, a genius, or even autistic. The particular label selected may largely depend on how that person performs in other aspects of intelligence. In any analysis of intelligence it would clearly be good for all aspects to be taken into account. Is this more rounded approach achievable? Yes, a completely new method of assessing intelligence, which does just this, is described in the next chapter.

9

THE HYPERSPHERE
OF INTELLIGENCE

A S WE HAVE REPEATEDLY DISCOVERED, intelligence is an extremely complex, multi-faceted entity. In each individual it consists of many different aspects, such as mathematical, creative, problem-solving, language, etc. To represent this range of distinctly different skills by means of one number (an IQ score) is surely gross over-simplification.

While a present-day IQ test may give an indication of some of the abilities possessed by an individual, it certainly does not do what it claims. Intelligence cannot be meaningfully represented by a single number. Individuals exhibit clear physical differences. Some are faster or weaker, while others simply cannot achieve certain physical feats. Some individuals are gymnasts, while others are couch potatoes. Would we consider describing someone's multi-faceted physical abilities by one number, a PQ? No, of course not.

So, is it possible to represent the intelligence of an individual in some meaningful way? Yes – it can be done by means of the hypersphere of intelligence, which is introduced here for the first time.

The Dimensions of the Hypersphere

Each dimension or plane of the hypersphere represents an individual's ability in one particular area – mathematics has a dimension, musical ability has a dimension, and so on. Within that dimension we can give an individual a more accurate score, which represents their ability solely in that area. The intelligence of an individual, in its entirety, is represented by a point in the hypersphere of intelligence, which brings together all the different dimensions.

In order to explain this further, let us begin by considering only verbal reasoning and mental arithmetic. In Figure 7.7 (see page 133) the horizontal axis indicates the individual's verbal reasoning skills, whilst the vertical axis depicts their mental arithmetic skills. The mid point in each case, possibly given the number 100, then indicates the norm, or population average, in that ability.

If an individual was above average in terms of mental arithmetic but below average in verbal reasoning, they would be positioned in Quadrant A. Quadrant D meanwhile would contain individuals who are above average on verbal reasoning but below average on mental arithmetic. The circle has been drawn to indicate the extremes. Positioning inside the circle indicates behaviour acceptable to society. Positioning outside the circle indicates abnormal behaviour, either because of very high or very low performance in at least one discipline. This could be due to eccentricity or a mental disorder of some kind.

In order to obtain a full 'map', each characteristic deemed to be a constituent factor in intelligence is denoted by a separate dimension in the hypersphere, the centre of which indicates idealised, normal behaviour in all respects. The outer edge of the hypersphere, represented by the circle in two dimensions, then indicates the boundary of characteristics which are deemed by society to be acceptable.

The actual number of dimensions employed in a hypersphere of intelligence is, however, subjective to the person constructing the hypersphere. You, the reader, may decide that there are twenty factors that are particularly important – thereby giving your hypersphere twenty dimensions. Another person meanwhile may feel that 1000 dimensions are more appropriate. This is, of course, due to the inherent subjective nature of intelligence. It is extremely doubtful whether society as a whole would ever be able to agree on a particular number of dimensions. Someone, somewhere will always disagree with the total number.

Howard Gardner, Professor of Education at Harvard University, has postulated seven types of intelligence. His theory of Multiple Intelligence lists these as follows:

1. Linguistic (reading writing)
2. Logical – Mathematical (patterns, relationships)
3. Bodily – Kinesthetic (crafts, sensations)
4. Spatial (images, jigsaws)
5. Musical (sounds, beats)
6. Interpersonal (communication, understanding)
7. Intrapersonal (self-motivation)

He nevertheless defines intelligence, in a more general way, as 'the capacity to solve problems or to fashion products that are valued in one or more cultural settings'.[1] He arrived at this theory by realising that there is both a biological and cultural basis for intelligence.

The problem with stipulating a specific number of well-defined disciplines is that it can be immediately challenged. For example, some might argue that certain of these seven disciplines can be sub-divided, other disciplines should also be included, and that – if we are considering intelligence in general – less of a human bias should be employed. Gardner has in fact recently added two further categories to this list, namely:

8. Recognising natural objects
9. Existential (pondering fundamental questions)

Whilst agreeing with the general thrust of Gardner's approach, I believe that finer divisions are likely to give a much more accurate picture. The approach introduced here allows all aspects of intelligence to be included.

PLOTTING POINTS IN A HYPERSPHERE

To explain further, in Figure 7.7 (see page 133) two dots appear in Quadrant A. These have been used to indicate the intelligence, solely in terms of the two factors being considered, of two parents. The children of these parents will, most likely, have an intelligence which is nearer the centre of the circle, i.e. nearer the norm. Some of their children could easily flip outside the circle and consequently be classed as mentally subnormal in some way. Essentially it appears that the brain can simply get stretched too far in a particular direction and, as a result, become unable to do some things acceptably.

Just as the points in Quadrant A of the two-dimensional figure were used to indicate the intelligence of two people, so, in the multi-dimensional hypersphere, a person's intelligence can be represented by a point in that multi-dimensional space. If, for example, it is considered that intelligence has fifty different aspects, resulting in fifty dimensions, then an individual's intelligence will have fifty different

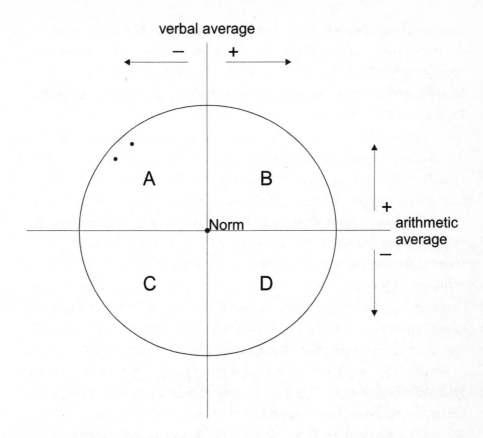

Figure 7.7: Hypersphere of Intelligence

values associated with it, resulting in a point positioned in the hypersphere. This makes it very difficult to compare dissimilar individuals, other than in one, or a small number of dimensions (for example, by comparing only their mathematical abilities). Thus it is difficult to compare an artist with a scientist, as their key intelligence points lie in completely different planes of the hypersphere, yet this is exactly what we try to do in life.

The intelligence of a genius would probably be somewhere near the edge of the hypersphere, due to their outstanding performance in a small number of the dimensions (for instance, if the person is solely a musical genius). In some cases, an individual can exceed the normal boundary due to environmental factors and/or biological changes in the brain. This latter event may occur with senility (due to ageing) or because of an accident, when certain parts of the brain start functioning in strange ways. It might therefore be a gradual change or a sudden one.

The hypersphere of intelligence concept also holds true for other creatures and even machines. In each case some of the dimensions may be the same as those of humans, others may be different. From our point of view, some creatures may appear to have more dimensions than us, whilst others may have less. We may have dimensions that other creatures do not have. This makes it very difficult to compare different species, or compare humans and machines. It is only when the ability in one dimension can be compared that a respectable analysis can be made. However, even this limited comparison presents difficulties and can easily become very subjective. For example how do you compare the musical abilities of a human, a bat, and a machine? To begin with, we would have to understand more about the meaning of music for bats and machines and not just impose a human understanding of music.

Relating your own intelligence to a point in a hypersphere can be rather difficult, particularly as humans find it hard to conceptualise anything above three or four dimensions. An alternative approach is therefore to plot all the different dimensions of interest as a two-dimensional rosette (see Figure 7.8).

In the rosette, each element of intelligence points out from a zero origin. Hence A could relate to mental arithmetic, E to verbal reasoning, H to musical ability, I to artistic creativity, and O to spatial awareness, the remaining spokes indicating whichever other intelligence characteristics we felt were relevant.

The centre point of the rosette represents zero, or no ability whatsoever. As with IQ testing, we can say that a score of 100 on, say, verbal reasoning or spatial awareness indicates average behaviour in that particular aspect of intelligence. Hence the dotted circle shown in Figure 7.8 represents a score of 100 in all aspects of intelligence. This would be the intelligence hypersphere of someone who is completely average in all their mental processes. The inner and outer circles then indicate the limits of normality. A score inside or outside these circles depicts abnormal intelligence in that field.

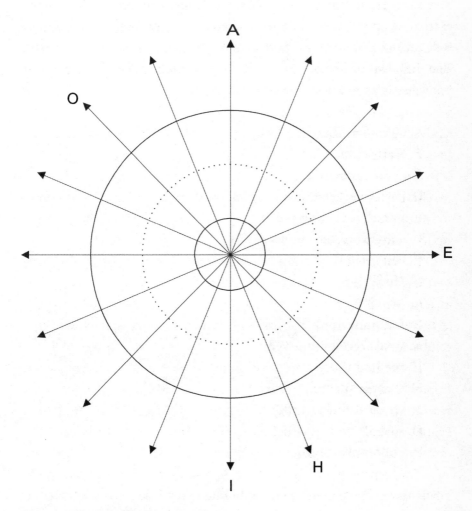

Figure 7.8: Intelligence Rosette

Individual Hypershapes

We can see from Figure 7.8 that everyone has their own hypershape of intelligence. Being above average in a particular area takes you outside the 100 circle, whereas being below average takes you inside the circle, for that particular ability.

In order to show this concept of hypershape in action I have, extremely subjectively, applied the rosette to myself, scoring myself well on the mathematical and verbal, but not so well on the artistic. The full list of spokes, with my (completely fictitious) scores in brackets, is as follows:

A. Mental arithmetic (130)

B. Mathematics (125)

C. Imagination (125)

D. Personnel/relationship skills (120)

E. Verbal reasoning (120)

F. Crosswords/anagrams (115)

G. Patterns (105)

H. Music (95)

I. Art (85)

J. Sculpture (88)

K. Word recognition (92)

L. Spelling (86)

M. Strategy/planning (95)

N. Physical fitness (100)

O. Spatial awareness (110)

P. Philosophy (120)

From these figures my own, individual hypershape is indicated in Figure 7.9, showing a leaning to the numerical. Unfortunately my scores have to be fictitious because it isn't possible to provide a hypersphere intelligence test in the present book. It would require at least another volume to present sufficient questions on a wide enough variety of mental skills to begin to give a useful measure of intelligence. I hope that, in the future, continuing research in the field will make such a test available. But, unlike an IQ test, I do not envisage it as a static, linear entity. A hypersphere intelligence test would need to be highly flexible, to suit the needs and abilities of the individual.

Every living person has an intelligence and hence every person has their own hypershape. One particular shape is not necessarily better or worse than any other, it is simply different. A larger hypershape area merely shows good ability in a wide range of characteristics; it does not mean that an individual is talented at anything in particular.

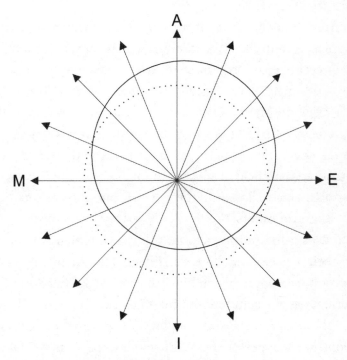

Figure 7.9: Kevin Warwick's Hypershape

Viewing intelligence in terms of a hypersphere gives a worth to all individuals. Everyone is on the map, with their own individual hypershape. Everyone has value. Even those who have little or no ability in one or a number of areas, merely lose out in those areas. Their hypershape can still reflect areas where they do have ability.

The Implications of the Intelligence Hypersphere

The hypersphere and hypershape concepts can be applied not only to humans, but also to machines. How does a machine's hypershape look on the human hypersphere? Can machines perform well on all spokes of the rosette, or do they score *nil points* in some dimensions? And, if so, is this important? These questions will be looked at closely in Chapter 12.

Returning, for the moment, to human intelligence, how far does all this get us in our quest for intelligence? It seems that intelligence *can* be represented as a hypersphere, with each different aspect indicated by a different plane. Inside the sphere (which corresponds to the outer circle in Figure 7.8), we have normal behaviour, allowing for individuals to perform better or worse than average as they move towards the edge of the sphere. A genius is certainly near the edge in one dimension, their field of specialisation. Some of the *autistic savants* discussed earlier are also near the edge in one dimensions but very near the centre in others.

IQ tests attach a number to an individual which is supposed to indicate their level of intelligence. Effectively, an IQ test attempts to reduce a hypersphere of intelligence to a single dimension, with a single number as the solution. But intelligence can potentially include millions of different facilities, requiring the same vast number of dimensions to its hypersphere. With standard IQ tests we subjectively select a small number of these by applying a few specific tests. But, by looking at those outside the normal boundaries (such as geniuses and people with autism), we can see that the picture is much more complex than this.

Can we say that people with certain disabilities are less intelligent than those without these disabilities? What about cerebral palsy, deafness or blindness? Just because these individuals are different from the norm in a particular way does not mean that they are not as intelligent as others. It merely means that they perform differently in different planes of the hypersphere; they have a different hypershape of intelligence. For instance, a blind person would be unable to score well on a picture recognition test, but they might achieve very high marks for mental arithmetic.

Why are people with a physical disability thought to be unintelligent? One of the world's most famous intellectuals, Stephen Hawking, cannot walk, talk directly for himself, feed himself or dress himself, yet he is one of the acknowledged leaders in the study of theoretical physics, author of the best-selling book *A Brief History of Time* and holds the post of Lucasian Professor of Mathematics at the University of Cambridge (a post once held by Sir Isaac Newton). Amazingly, he has achieved all this whilst being confined to a wheelchair due to a progressive motor neurone disease. However, if we were to look at this man without knowing who he was, would we immediately regard him as being intelligent? Probably not; probably quite the reverse.

Why do we so often look at external appearance and make a judgement on what is on the inside? In Stephen Hawking's case we might mistakenly consider him to be stupid because he has physical disabilities. Likewise, we might consider autistic people to be stupid because we have not yet discovered what special abilities they have. Clearly, we must not let physical differences colour our view of intelligence; we must look closely at mental abilities, otherwise our conclusions will be biased.

But, having said this, human intelligence is nevertheless dependent not only on our mental make-up, but also on who and what we are physically. Our human view of intelligence is limited by our human abilities, both physical and mental. Our intelligence is suitable for our bodies and our environment. And this is also true of other animals and insects. Each species has evolved both mentally and physically, in its own balanced way.

How is the intelligence of a creature affected by the body it is in and how does this relate to our overall picture of intelligence? What does it mean for a horse or cow to be intelligent? Can we really compare such intelligence directly with that of a human? The next chapter continues the quest – into the animal world.

10

ANIMAL
INTELLIGENCE

A S HUMANS, WE LIKE TO THINK OF ourselves as being uniquely intelligent. We feel there is something special about the ways in which we think, plan, learn, and communicate with each other, and in how the human brain consciously operates. But recent research into other species has made us realise that they, too, are capable of complex thought processes and behaviour. Furthermore, we can now make machines that also display complex behaviour patterns and problem-solving skills.

In the past, our ability to reason was seen as something which set humans apart from other creatures. Many years ago, the suggestion that other animals could consciously think would have been considered heresy. However, we have now seen that other creatures and machines *can* exhibit complex behaviour similar to our own. We must question whether certain abilities, which we have previously associated with intelligence, are so important after all. By looking closely at other creatures, and comparing them with ourselves and with highly advanced machines, we can perhaps gain a better understanding of what actually constitutes intelligent behaviour.

Human intelligence used to be compared with that of other species in terms of a 'mental ladder'. Humans were on top, primates a few rungs down, and amoebae at the bottom. Now this is seen to be a limited and perhaps even false view. Whilst comparisons can certainly be made in this way, with regard to the number of brain cells and their connectivity, in each species, as we have seen, intelligence is best viewed as a hypersphere, rather than a single-dimensional ladder. In fact the ladder concept links closely with a single 'IQ score' idea of intelligence.

We must remember that intelligence in each species is appropriate for that species. Some abilities in a species may be almost equal to those of humans, others may be distinctly better, and still others may not relate at all to human intelligence as we now perceive it. Often, when another species clearly outperforms human beings in a particular area of ability we tend to downplay the importance of those abilities, sometimes to the extent of disregarding them completely.

BEHAVIOURISM VERSUS CONSCIOUSNESS

In studying the mental processes of other species we can only investigate from the outside, looking at behaviours and responses. It is therefore difficult to repeat observations or to force different individuals in a particular species to undergo identical clinical trials in order to thoroughly test a particular hypothesis. For example, a creature may tackle the same problem as a human but do so in a very different way.

One important lesson was learnt in the case of a horse named Hans, whose behaviour was studied by Oskar Pfungst, a researcher at the Psychological Clinic in Berlin.[1] Hans could point out directions, count from 1 to 100 by tapping his right hoof, walk in the direction of a requested object and even tap out coded numbers for playing cards (one tap for an Ace, two for a King and so on). Extensive studies appeared to show that Hans had, due to intensive training, mastered the art of abstract thought. Many expert groups tested the horse, and it was concluded that no trickery was involved. Further studies by Pfungst, however, revealed an alternative solution. It appeared that Hans was actually looking for involuntary clues in his audience that almost always appeared when he reached the correct number of hoof taps, or walked in the right direction. Even slight smiles appeared to be accurately translated by Hans.

Quite surprisingly, the Hans incident was taken by some to mean that a mere horse had tricked philosophers and scientists alike into coming to an 'egg-on-face' conclusion as far as animal intelligence was concerned. The fact that Hans, who perceived the world from a horse's point of view had observed connections not actually spotted by humans, and had perhaps solved the problem in a different way from a human, appears to have been largely overlooked.

In the latter part of the nineteenth century it was believed by some, such as British psychologist George Romanes, that even shell-fish could perceive relationships and act on the results of their perceptions. In his book *Animal Intelligence* he argued that just about all living creatures could exhibit reason,[2] claiming that 'an oyster is able to perceive new relations and suitably to act upon the results of its perceptions'. He believed it was reason, and not so much instinct, that drove even these creatures.

Possibly because of the Hans incident, in the first half of the twentieth century opinion swung violently in the opposite direction, to the extent that the existence of free will and conscious thought in all animals (including humans) was denied! The founder of this school of thought, termed behaviourism, was John Watson, an

American psychologist. In 1912 he said, 'Consciousness is neither a definite nor a usable concept,' and that belief in its existence, 'goes back to the ancient days of superstition and magic'.[3] Even learning in humans was, according to the behaviourist view, regarded as being automatic, no conscious understanding being necessary.

The behaviourist approach now took firm hold. Just as Pavlov's dog could be taught to associate food with a bell sounding,[4] so it was believed that an individual could be conditioned through a series of rewards and punishments to behave in a particular way.

Many of the issues raised in the debate on conscious thought versus behaviourism are still relevant today. If a human is conscious, then surely a dog is too, in which case a bee must also be, and so on – down to an amoeba and beyond! Conversely, if an amoeba cannot think consciously then how can a human? Could it be that some creatures exhibit conscious thought and others act in a behaviouristic way? If so, where do we draw the line? John Searle, a leading philosopher, feels that, 'it is probably not useful to worry about such questions'.[5]

This argument about consciousness in living species has now spilt over into the world of machines. Many people say that a machine cannot be truly intelligent if it is not conscious, but how do we define consciousness? At Reading we have a six-legged robot, Elma, that learns to walk and reacts to objects in her path. She certainly exhibits an innate, behaviourist form of intelligence. But can she, in any way, be said to be conscious and able to reason about the world around her? Some, such as Searle, refuse to even consider the matter, saying of robots, 'I think the idea they might be conscious is simply out of the question.' Yet Elma has a similarly designed nervous system to that of a cockroach. Is it really possible to draw a line between upper and lower animals, or between humans and robots, or animals and robots, and claim that one has some superior form of intelligence? We will investigate this in Chapter 12.

TELEPATHY AND ANIMAL INTELLIGENCE

Over the years some animal studies have resulted in a questioning of not only the behaviourist approach to animal intelligence but also of the fundamentals of science itself. One such example is provided by yet another horse, this time called Lady Wonder, who lived between 1924 and 1952, in the USA.[6] Lady used her muzzle to manipulate blocks to form words. Two people would separately write words only known to them, on respective pads of paper. Without seeing the words Lady could spell them out by manipulating the blocks. The talents of Lady, incorporating telepathy, were investigated in depth by many professional experts, who all supported her case!

By the 1950s it was found that Lady could accurately answer questions about lost objects and even missing people. In 1952 Lady predicted that a missing child would be found at a place called Pittsfield Water Wheel. Subsequently the underwater quarry at Field and Wilde Water Pit was dragged and the child's body found. Later that year extensive searches failed to locate a small boy and girl who had gone missing from their home in Napierville, Illinois, USA. Lady indicated that they were in fact already dead, and correctly pointed to the Dupage River as their location. The children's mother, who had first turned to Lady for help, later said, 'The horse was right about everything but the day they would be found.'[7]

However, telepathy is something that we, as humans, have little or no understanding of. Because of this it tends to get discounted, and is usually thought of as mere trickery. Certainly we do not regard telepathic ability as being, in any way, linked to intelligence. But it may be that some other species use telepathy as a regular means of communication, although we have, to my knowledge, no way of detecting whether or not this is the case. How many abilities do other species have that we humans put no value on? And how many of their abilities are not even known to us?

TOOL USE IN PRIMATES

One common method of looking for signs of intelligence in other species is to consider how far they exhibit human-like characteristics in their daily life. Perhaps this is why other apes, particularly chimpanzees, are often considered a good species to study. (The chimpanzee, in particular, is regarded as a very close human relative, sharing 98.5 per cent of our DNA). Their view of the world, their interaction with it, and with each other, is most like that of humans.

Chimps are famed as tool-makers and users. They strip leaves off twigs in order to use them as probes for ants. By inserting them into a termite mound they 'fish' for the termites which cling to the twig. They also use sticks to release nuts from shells and to pick out bits of brain from a skull. Leaves are used as plates for food, to clean themselves with, in crushed form as a sponge to gather water or ants, and as a device to catch their faeces for later inspection.[8] Tool behaviour in chimps does, however, appear to be innate. No technological advances appear from one generation to the next, although they do learn the best places to use the tools, one chimp guiding another to a fruitful location which is then remembered.

Chimps can also tackle a problem they have not previously encountered, using the tools at their disposal. Stealing honey appears to provide just such a challenge, due to the variety in type and position of bees' nests. In one study a chimpanzee in Gambia used four different types of tool in sequence in order to extract honey from the nest of a stingless bee, in a tree hollow.[9] However, the problem with such studies is that it remains very difficult for humans to analyse the situation from a non-human position. In order to get to the honey has the chimp come up with something genuinely new or has she simply used her innate abilities in a particular way? Only the chimp knows the true answer.

PLANNING AND ABSTRACT THOUGHT

Foraging for food provides a very fertile ground for studies on planning and reasoning in animals. One interesting case that has recently come to light is that of green herons. The natural way for a heron to catch fish is by diving steeply and quickly, but a more devious approach has occasionally been witnessed. Some herons have been seen to drop small morsels of food into the water where fish are expected to be; when a fish swims to take up the bait the heron then catches it. This method is both simple and highly successful, and yet is not commonly encountered. In fact the habit tends to appear and to die out with one bird, not spreading to others. It is felt that some herons learn to fish in this way despite the fact that they are not genetically programmed to do so. Whatever the case, as it is a successful pastime, evolutionary effects could take hold and make some green herons innately more likely to learn such a trait than others.[10]

To return to primates, chimps appear to retain some sort of mental map of likely food productive areas and other resources. This ability enables a group in the wild to direct itself to particular areas that are resource-rich. Their 'maps' also seem to be seasonably adjusted, to allow for fruits ripening at different times, with additions being made to the maps as new resources appear. All this indicates that chimps can observe environmental features and remember them with considerable accuracy.

It has also been found that Tai chimpanzees plan hunting trips.[11] Planned hunting behaviour has been witnessed long before any prey (colobus monkey) is actually apparent. The chimps hunt as a group: they scatter in order to cover all avenues of escape, and only gather together when a victim is cornered. Such an approach requires an agreed plan, with discipline amongst members, as well as coordination and collaboration within the group.

These are some of the key behavioural characteristics which, in the past, made us feel superior to all other living species. We believed it was only humans who were capable of forethought, coordination among individuals and successful execution of previously laid out plans. But now we see that other species are also capable of such behaviour. Not only this but some *machines* are able to work in teams, communicate with each other, and even search for a source of energy. Where does this leave our assumptions concerning our innately superior intelligence?

Chimps are known to share out food. When prey is caught or fruit is picked, by adult males, the others come looking for their share which they generally receive. Only in times of hardship does quarrelling between the adult males take place; while, under difficult circumstances, females tend to share food only with their own children or close friends.

Other species tend to perform very differently as far as food is concerned. Bernd Heinrich, from the University of Vermont, hand-reared five ravens. In a recent experiment he suspended pieces of meat by strings from the ravens' perches. The strings were too long for the ravens to pick at the meat from their perch and so they tried to fly past it and capture it in this way. However, it was too securely fixed. After about six hours some of the ravens had given up, but one of them discovered that it could stand on the perch and pull up an amount of string, trap it beneath its claws, reach down and pull up another amount, and so on, eventually getting to its rich meat prize. No period of trial and error learning appeared to take place. It just happened.

Several days later a second raven solved the problem in a slightly different way, stretching the string out on the perch until the meat could be reached. Later, another looped the string onto the perch and obtained the meat in that way. Each bird, except for one who never solved the problem at all, found a different solution for themselves, none of them apparently benefiting from the experience of a successful colleague.[12]

If an individual human being is given a particular problem and, without watching another individual or experimenting in any way, simply comes up with a successful solution one presumes they have used a fair amount of abstract thought. If a raven behaves in the same way it implies that ravens too can think things out, and plan, in abstract terms.

IMPROVISATION AND DECEPTION

Jean Piaget, the French child psychologist, once said that intelligence is what you use when you do not know what to do. This places a firm emphasis on dealing with the unexpected; in situations where there is not simply one correct answer, invention, novelty, improvisation and creativity may be required. Dogs have many innate behaviours, such as barking an alarm or herding. However, merely tying their lead to a post usually provides them with too great a challenge, unless they have been specifically taught to deal with it. Chimps and many monkeys are, though, not so readily restrained. For chimps a padlock is required on a cage, with no key or long thin (lock-picking) object anywhere in reach.

Chimps can also sometimes guess what another animal is thinking and is likely to do, and they can even practise deception. In one group of observed chimps[13] Dandy, the youngest of the four grown males in the group was not allowed, by the lead male, to have sexual intercourse with any of the adult females, due to his lowly rank. Dandy did, however, still achieve success in this direction by orchestrating 'chance' meetings with females. Such encounters occurred after Dandy had exchanged glances with a female, sometimes going as far as slight physical contact, the actual meeting (and mating) subsequently taking place behind a tree, out of sight. Male chimps start the proceedings by sitting with their legs apart to reveal their erection. On one occasion, one of the older males, Luit, happened to catch Dandy in this flirtatious stage. Dandy immediately cupped his hands over his penis to hide the evidence.[14]

Sometimes Dandy and a mate would pretend to forage for berries, or the like, with their top halves open to general view, but with their bottom halves coupled together and hidden by undergrowth. One day Dandy rushed to the front of his enclosure, screaming at the human onlookers. The elder male chimps hastened across to see what all the commotion was about. Dandy sloped off in the ensuing confusion to find a willing female. On a separate occasion another younger chimp was spotted by Dandy, making advances to a female. Dandy's response was to quickly go and fetch the lead chimp, who dealt decisively and firmly with Dandy's competitor. Dandy undoubtedly appeared to be displaying an ability to plot, plan, reason and think, with clear goals in mind.

In other creatures it may be considered that deception is a genetically inherited feature, however it is quite surprising how behaviours can adapt to meet the situation. A number of ground nesting birds, such as plovers and killdeers, have to be particularly resourceful in order to survive. When a predator approaches, the bird's strategy is to get the predator well away from its nest and the eggs contained therein. Tactics can involve simply moving to open ground (where it can be readily seen), calling loudly in order to attract attention, and also running through undergrowth making mouse-like squeals, or even pretending to have a broken wing, therefore appearing to be easy prey. On the other hand they use a simple sudden noise strategy to startle relatively harmless creatures, such as deer, that could tread on their nest merely by accident.

The tactics used by such birds depend on the enemy at the time. In the late 1990s Carolyn Riston of Columbia University arranged for two distinctively dressed groups of humans to walk close by a collection of plover nests. While one group walked a safe path, appearing to pay no attention to the nests, the second group scanned the ground closely, searching at length. Before long the plovers paid little attention to individuals from the first group, yet proffered a full range of deception displays to members of the second group. In this case it is difficult to establish whether each bird learns particular tactics for itself or if they partly learn from observation of others.

LEARNING AND PLAYING

With all creatures other than humans it is difficult to decide if one individual learns from another, or whether particular habits gradually become hereditary over a number of generations. For example tools, such as hammers, are not unique to humans and chimps. Egyptian vultures use stones to crack the eggs of ground nesting birds, while some sea otters crack the shells of molluscs on stones they balance on their chest – themselves floating upside down at the time. Song thrushes also smash the shells of snails on stones, to get to the soft insides. In each case these skills appear to be innate, genetic, programed habits of the specific creature, rather than a learnt technique. Is this the case with all species other than our own?

On rare occasions chimpanzees have been observed to teach one another.[15] When witnessing their infant having difficulties in nut cracking, some mother chimps have been seen to demonstrate how to tackle the problem. In one instance an infant chimp was shown, by its parent, the 'correct' method of gripping a stone for hammering, the infant immediately responding by copying their parent. It is interesting too that, along with orang-utans, chimps can quickly pick up techniques when taught them by humans – hence weeding, bridge-building, canoeing, tooth-brushing, sweeping and even siphoning have all been learnt from humans.[16]

The ability to learn within a species can be seen as an innate, genetically inherited feature, the finishing touches only being added to fine-tune a particular skill or technique. It could therefore be considered that individuals are, by and large, in their final form when they are born, but that learning allows them to polish their innate behaviour. This leads us back to the recurring nature versus nurture argument.

Clearly animals can learn by observing, and so can robots (as we will see in Chapter 12), particularly when rewards and/or punishments are given. Is it so different when a human observes and learns, when a human copies, mimics or tries another route? Just because we are human it does not mean that the way we do things is 'automatically' better.

Even octopuses can learn. A 1992 study investigated one, untrained, octopus when it viewed a trained octopus through a glass partition.[17] The trained octopus chose between objects that differed in colour and subsequently opened a container which held tasty morsels. In consequence the untrained octopus was able to readily choose 'correctly' between the colours and to swiftly open the container, certainly much more quickly than a non-observing, untrained octopus.

Perhaps play in infants is also a way of experimenting with different strategies. In humans, play can be used to try out strategies for adulthood and perhaps even practise leadership behaviour. Many species exhibit play – wild cats, for example, fighting in a 'friendly' way. Ravens have been witnessed throwing pebbles to each other, beak to beak, in mid-air, and on occasions even sliding down a snow face. Parrots also enjoy snow (producing and launching snowballs) although they like swimming even more, particularly backstroke! Octopuses squirt jets of water at objects bobbing on the surface, whilst many creatures (including sheep, horses, whales and dolphins) leap into the air – just for fun.

DOLPHIN AND WHALE INTELLIGENCE

Dolphins provide us with something of a quandary. Because of their 'friendly' nature they have been studied extensively and this has led many to conclude that they are truly intelligent creatures, some even say on a par with humans.[18,19]

The picture of dolphin intelligence is by no means clear, yet it does give us an indication of the difficulties that arise when comparing the intelligence of different species. Dolphins clearly interact with their environment in a different way to humans because of their different physical characteristics, but what does this mean in terms of intelligence?

When marked with a zinc oxide spot dolphins have been found to twist and make open-mouthed head movements in order to, apparently, inspect the mark, by means of a 1.2 metre (4 foot) diameter mirror, for a short period.[20] Conversely, dolphins have been known to spend over 99 per cent of their time interacting with a person, even for long periods. One problem with the mirror test is knowing whether or not the dolphin is responding to its own image. The range of signals given, such as posturing and open-mouth head movements, are also the type of signals given when a dolphin is excited by or even threatened by another dolphin.

Although humans may put value on responding to their image in a mirror, it could be that for other creatures this is of little or no value at all. Indeed, even amongst humans, it would seem odd to suggest that those humans who spend most of their time inspecting themselves in the mirror are much more intelligent. With dolphins, in fact, all indications are that looking in a mirror is of little value, apart, maybe, from having some fun.

In 1979 a test was carried out by Gordon Gallup, Professor and Chair of Psychology at the State University of New York at Albany, in which two male bottlenose dolphins, Keola and Hot Rod, were filmed as they swam. Each was, for some periods, shown a real-time image of themselves on a wide screen, and for other periods a record-ed image. Keola tended to perform for the camera, swimming around, making head and mouth gestures, something which he did not seem to do when the video showing was recorded. While Hot Rod's behaviour was generally not so distinctive, on one occasion, after being fed, he swam up to the screen, stuck a fish out of his mouth – where it could be clearly seen by the camera – and promptly sucked it back in again.[21]

Dolphins gain respect from humans for their ability to solve problems and for their memory capabilities. They have a relatively large brain size to body ratio and it is suggested that, along with porpoises and whales, their roots lie in a forty-million-year-old family. The theory is that the collective group, known as cetaceans, actually lived on land for about ten million years before this. Interestingly, the foetus of a whale appears to contain hands and fingers, which fuse together shortly before birth.

A human brain has a large cortex region used for memory, computing and context. Dolphins have similar areas and have been extensively tested using words broadcast through an underwater speaker. These words refer to objects, places and actions such as ball and hoop. With two-word (or sometimes rather longer) sentence instructions the dolphin must respond accordingly, having something like a 600-word vocabulary in total. An 80 per cent accurate response is typically obtained, although sometimes the dolphin must be told twice. Sentences can in fact be up to five words long and both visual and auditory symbols can be employed. This is, of course, all operating on human terms.

It is certainly not true to say that dolphin brains are simlar to ours. Their structure is more akin to that of primitive mammals, such as hedgehogs or bats. A dolphin's cortex regions are not separated, as in primates, but resemble more closely those of mammal ancestors.[22] As with whales, studies have occasionally indicated a respectable degree of intelligence in some areas. However, for the most part this is not the case. In common with fish, the brain functioning and intelligence of cetaceans seems to predate that of humans and other primates by several million years. As they have already inhabited the Earth for so much longer than us, they may well have a method of surviving that will ultimately outlast our own.

It is interesting that, while we humans tend to set great store by the ability of other creatures to understand human language, we appear to ignore our own lack of understanding of other species. For example whale song is different around the world, is complex and appears to be based on a set of inherited rules. A whale's song is the same during one year and then changes. Phrases in a song consist of two to five different sounds, a song being made up of six themes each with phrases in the same order. A song's duration may be anything from six to thirty minutes and it sounds amazingly like birdsong, when recorded and speeded up fourteen or fifteen times.[23] Yet, even after studying it at length for many years, humans have made little sense of it.

COMMUNICATION AND VISUAL SKILLS IN BIRDS

Whale song may differ considerably around the world, but with birdsong there is even greater variety. Talking ability differs enormously between parrots. While one bird may learn to speak several words at a very early age, another may never learn the habit. Like most birds, parrots are very social creatures, a trait which even enables them to get on with humans. Wild parrots appear to 'know' all the others in their flock, rejecting or killing strangers.

However, parrots are not the only birds that communicate with humans. Even wild birds can form a close association with people when treated with respect and provided regularly with food. Len Howard conducted an eleven-year study from her cottage in the English countryside. Her conclusions were that:[24]

1. Birds of the same species can be distinguished because they have their own distinct movements, habits, personalities and even emotions.
2. Birds of the same species, sex and age can vary widely in how they behave.

Clearly birds are very much individuals, with easily recognisable distinctions between them when they are studied. This goes very much against the idea that such creatures are mindless or 'programmed' with no feelings.

As we consider the nature of consciousness and intelligence in creatures other than humans, it becomes very clear that it is incorrect to assign such characteristics to humans alone. In fact when we consider particular features of human intelligence that we feel are important, we play a dangerous game. Quite often a relatively simple creature can exhibit similar characteristics in its own way. But, as humans, we are very subjective about the way we rank different aspects of intelligence, tying them in closely to our own strengths and weaknesses. Other creatures can often outperform humans at particular feats. The fact that humans find those feats difficult or impossible to accomplish does not make the achievements unimportant.

Migrating and homing birds, such as pigeons, it appears, find their way by integrating a variety of natural information, such as movement of the sun and the stars, the earth's magnetic field, visual landmarks, cloud movements and wind direction.[25] It has also been found that birds of the same species can use different information in order to arrive at the same destination. Not only that but the same bird can use different information at different times, for the same journey.

Some fascinating studies with pigeons have shown that they can also recognise a particular human under various disguises, such as when the person wears strange clothes or is nude, or even when they are merely a small face on a large group photograph.[26] Pigeons can also be taught to recognise objects (such as trees) from a range of pictures by being rewarded with food when they pecked at any picture with, for example, a tree in it. In some instances the pigeons have apparently been able to memorise hundreds of pictures where no common object is involved. However, when there is a common feature they can learn this quite credibly, responding correctly to a new set of pictures and even making critical judgements when the feature varies from picture to picture.

MAKING COMPARISONS

Just as we must take care, as humans, not to belittle the capabilities and intelligence of other entities (whether animal or machine), we must also ensure that we do not misrepresent the case of the other creature in other ways. For example, I recently came across a statement about pigs which said, 'By the time they are full grown, pigs have the intelligence of a 6- to 7-year-old human.'[27] Such a statement is very difficult to comprehend, and even more difficult to substantiate. While it may well be true that we usually credit pigs with too little intelligence, it is impossible to see how such a conclusion can be drawn.

Pigs naturally live in groups and have a well-defined social order, but they do not appear to have the same complexity of communication as chimpanzees, dolphins or various birds. Pigs do have a larger brain, for their body size, than other farm animals such as sheep and cows. They are also richer in the area that seems to deal with reasoning. And there appears to be more psychology involved in dealing with pigs. Whereas scolding a dog, chimp or horse may get them to learn, with a pig such an action invariably results in the pig hurling the abuse right back.[28]

One interesting test is the Bar Harbor maze in which various animals were tested in a maze to see how long it took them to find their way around.[29] Cats did not wish to participate at all; dogs, horses and chickens could be taught a solution reasonably well, but pigs turned out to be the winners, due to their 'capacity for independent thinking and ability to figure out a problem for themselves.'[30] Between animals it is difficult to compare intelligence, due to the different abilities each animal has. On specific tests, such as the maze, direct comparisons can be made, although they still only tell us about the animal's abilities in relation to that particular problem.

ELEPHANTS AND EMOTIONS

While pigs may well be difficult for humans to understand, the elephant provides us with a clearer picture of how an animal's intelligence has evolved as an integral part of the overall creature. Elephants have a wonderful sense of smell (which far outstrips the human sense of smell) and this is used for social meetings as well as to spot danger. Their sight is relatively poor. However, they can communicate using touch, smell and sound, although interactive visual gestures have also been witnessed. Their trunk is not only responsible for making sounds such as puffing, trumpeting and blowing, but is also used for smell sensing as it can be waved in the air or positioned as required.

Elephants communicate over very long distances using low-frequency sounds (another area in which they out-perform humans). As a result they have been known to co-ordinate foraging within a group dispersed over a wide area. Their noises are varied and manifold and appear to indicate moods, desires and plans. Simpler signals, within human hearing, such as trumpeting, are used sometimes merely to indicate location, so that a group can stick together. In fact elephants, by and large, are very social creatures, travelling in groups up to thousands strong. Like humans and chimps, elephants use tools (such as branches to swat flies). They also dig holes, several metres deep, when searching for water.

One of the most striking aspects of elephants' behaviour is their incredible feelings for each other (a characteristic to which humans like to think we have exclusive claim). Recently a park warden told of a female elephant continuing to carry around her small calf even though it had been dead for several days. She placed it on the ground when she drank water or ate. The rest of her group appeared to appreciate her dilemma and slowed down their movement to wait for her to overcome her grief.[31]

Cynthia Moss, who has studied wild African elephants at length, told of what happened when she brought the jawbone of a dead adult female into her camp, in order to determine its age. The dead elephant's family made a detour to the camp, apparently to examine the bone. When the rest of the group had moved on, the female's seven-year-old calf stayed behind repeatedly turning the bone over with his feet and trunk.[32]

HORSES FOR COURSES

The different sensory and mental abilities of other species make it difficult for humans to understand what exactly is going on in the mind of another creature: why are they thinking in a certain way and how they perceive the world. On the one hand, we should not anthropomorphise and endow other creatures with human-like emotions. But, on the other hand, it is very difficult for us to gain any understanding of the motivation behind another creature's actions unless we do so. When a creature's range of abilities is well beyond that of a human, as is the case with elephants, it becomes difficult for us to comprehend their actions. For example, why should they be so interested in bones, and how does the information gleaned from inspecting a bone affect them?

Just as the way in which other creatures, such as dolphins and elephants, perceive the world is quite different from the way humans perceive it, so intelligence, which is inextricably linked to the senses, reflects each creature's physical attributes. As each species has evolved, so their intelligence has evolved as part of that process. Each species is successful in its own way; the fact that the species exists at all is proof of that. Every species will have its own hypersphere of intelligence. Common axes do exist, but it becomes difficult to make inter-species comparisons. For example, how do you rank the smell abilities of an elephant with those of a parrot, dog, robot or human?

Because intelligence in each species is an integral part of that species' make-up, attempting to make comparisons between species is fraught with problems. In particular, when humans carry out such a comparison it is impregnated with human values and a human perspective. Comparisons are made between characteristics that humans regard as important. Such a stance is, of course, biased and subjective to human intelligence. Just as comparisons between humans are distorted by individual subjectivity, so comparisons with other creatures are distorted by human species subjectivity.

For example, the ability to understand human speech is taken as a sign of intelligence in other species. Yet we do not see it as a sign of incompetence that we cannot understand the noises made by a cat or whale. We appear to appreciate the fact that other creatures can do things physically that we cannot, but seem to belittle the way those other creatures sense the world and communicate within it, when their abilities are outside the normal range for us. Each sentient creature houses a complex intelligence, with attributes that are relevant to that creature. This is true of *all* creatures, and understanding this simple concept appears to be crucial to understanding intelligence.

Different creatures sense the world in different ways. Some live in water, some on land and some in both. Deciding what is innate in a creature, and what is not, is fraught with problems; what is a basic behaviour and what requires conscious thought? In comparing intelligence, what are the critical factors? Perhaps we need to examine this question at a more basic level. Surely, in any species, the ability of individuals to control their own destiny is important – survival is paramount.

We have seen how animals and birds of various types display their intelligence, but what of insects? Can they be said to be conscious or intelligent too? Perhaps we can learn more, particularly with regard to the success of a species, and basic intelligence, by considering insects – in the next chapter.

11

INSECT
INTELLIGENCE

ASSESSING THE INTELLIGENCE OF other humans is a complex
task, yet at least we all have the same range of sensory mechanisms and actuators (arms, legs, and so on). So tests can be arrived
at to compare individuals. With other animals and birds, as we saw
in Chapter 10, we can apply similar types of initiative or response
tests. Some of these tests are well targeted to a specific animal and
their abilities; others, such as problem-solving tasks, are much more
general in nature. In such cases, it is very easy to suppose that an
animal is carrying out a task in a human-like way, whether or not
any human-like decisions are really being made. Physical similarities
help the comparison, as with chimps painting or looking into a mirror.

In his essay 'What is it like to be a bat?',[1] Thomas Nagel asked:
how can we measure a bat's intelligence if we ourselves are not bats?
And how can we measure the intelligence based on our own experience and upbringing? This is the central problem which led to the

introduction of the Theory of Subjective Intelligence. The dilemma is due to the lack of a completely objective test for intelligence, either within a species or between species. In particular, physical characteristics vary enormously between species and intelligence takes very different forms.

Whilst – despite the difficulties – we can attempt to consider the intelligence of animals in relation to humans, with insects this rapidly becomes very difficult. For instance, one could start by looking at population size as an indication of success. According to this criterion, humans certainly compare well with other animals, totalling several billion around the world. However, the sheer quantity of different insects makes human numbers appear virtually insignificant. For example, *The Guinness Book of Records* (1999), reports that in 1874 one swarm of locusts in the Nebraska Rocky Mountain area of the USA contained an estimated 12.5 trillion insects.

In addition, the physical capabilities of insects are so different from our own that comparisons become almost impossible, as does the assessment of such capabilities in terms of intelligent acts. Bees and ants, for instance, display amazing collective, rather than individual, intelligence. Do these colonial insects act as a result of their communicated signals or purely instinctively? It's hard to say. But only at our peril do we regard their actions as insignificant.

The functioning of insects can be very different from that of other creatures. For example African termite queens are about 13 to 14 centimetres long and lay up to 30,000 eggs every day. Their entire life is spent in a royal cell in the colony centre, their role being purely that of egg producer. Mayflies, meanwhile, spend two to three years as sucklings at the bottom of pools. When they eventually reach maturity, their total adult life lasts for about an hour. The smell sensing capabilities of the male emperor moth are triggered by as little as one molecule of attractant carried by the female, who can be a distance of over 10 kilometres away.

In each of these cases it is almost impossible to make any direct comparison with humans. Physical characteristics and capabilities are hugely different, as are the associated requirements of each creature's brain. It is impossible to say that one creature is 'better' or 'worse' than another, unless we consider broad measures such as the length of time that a species has existed or its total population size.

ANT INTELLIGENCE

In order to investigate the intellectual capabilities of insects, we will consider here a number of examples. Perhaps then we can more readily balance up the pros and cons. For example, the collective power of ants is often much admired by humans. One particular feature is the way that ants can follow along a particular track, collecting and retrieving food and nest-building material. As it moves, each ant releases a chemical substance, called pheromone, which can be detected by other ants of the same type.

It is widely accepted that ants lay down their own pheromone, while following what appears to be the strongest such trail already deposited. In this way, a profitable trail gets strengthened as more and more ants follow it. If an object appears in the path then, by a process of trial and error, an alternative route around the object is soon settled on. When a source of food dries up, so too does the path from that food to the nest. Very quickly a new, food-rich, path takes precedence as more and more ants travel by that route. Ants which do not adhere closely to the trail are less likely to reach the food sources and thus can perhaps be regarded, in terms of AI (Ant Intelligence), as less intelligent.

Leaf-cutting ants, found mainly in South and Central America, not only follow pheromone trails but also communicate with each other by rubbing a file against their abdomen, creating a sound which is clearly audible to humans. This species also carries out a form of division of labour to tend their mushroom gardens, with different individuals performing different tasks. Some find leaves and some maintain a compost heap, whilst others expand the nest. This form of social behaviour in ant life appears critical to the colony's existence, males, females and different castes all having a unique role. Labour specialisation is something which is common to all ant colonies.

When considering human intelligence, this type of social behaviour has been seen by numerous researchers as a critical factor in the development of the human brain. However, the fact that ants (each with a brain about a ten-millionth the size of a human brain) also carry out such acts, tends to knock that theory firmly on the head.

Research into ant communication has indicated a wide range of signalling abilities. These include signals for the purposes of warning, attraction, grooming, recognition and discrimination, caste determination, territorial indicators, sexual communication . . . the list goes on. The underlying medium for all these signals is a chemical. In particular, those signals related to sex and production are extremely specific. It appears[2] that a colony operates most effectively when its members are genetically tightly knit. As a direct consequence of this, an ant which strays into a foreign colony is usually violently set upon: their mandibles are held whilst they are stung or sprayed with a toxic substance such as formic acid.

While these facts are interesting, how much do they tell us about intelligence? This is obviously a question open to interpretation. But what is clear is that ants only appear to have value as members of their colony. Individual behaviour is only of use in so far as it may turn up a new food source, for the good of the colony.

Tactile information between ants is limited. The antennae are used more for receipt of information (via smell) than for signalling by touch. Rhythmic body beating with antennae does occur, although little is known about its purpose or effect. Sound in the air has almost no effect on ants, but vibrations through the earth are used for alarm signals, during mating and even to indicate food sources or the location of a new nest.

It might be thought that all this behaviour is simply genetically programmed, but studies indicate that this is far from the truth. Although regurgitation and grooming do appear to be innate, orientation seems to be achievable not only through a pheromone trail but also through memorising visual landmarks. Ants clearly adapt their behaviour according to the state of the colony's food supply.

Like rats, ants are quite good at solving mazes. Not only that but they appear to accurately remember a correct solution for several days afterwards. Many ants use the sun's position to help them navigate, especially when winds or sandstorms have covered any pheromone trails. In 1911 Santschi[3] carried out a famous 'mirror experiment' on desert ants returning home with food. He shaded them from the sun on one side and, by means of a mirror, played the sun in the opposite direction. The ants dutifully marched in a direction 180° away from home. When the shade and mirror were removed, they immediately reversed direction and headed home. More recent experiments[4] have shown that ants can keep track of the sun's movements and constantly adjust their path. Similar results have been witnessed with bees.

By looking closely at ants, we can see a complex behavioural existence. What is due to nature, and what is due to nurture, is (as with humans) not clear. From the outside it might be concluded that most of an ant's characteristics can be clearly linked to innate abilities, with relatively few being due to learning. We must remember, however, that ants are very different from humans, and it is therefore extremely difficult to decipher much of their signalling. For example, does a particular wiggle mean something or not? It is also difficult to decide whether or not ants signal or behave in ways that do not have an immediately obvious purpose. If we can't spot the purpose, it is very easy to belittle or even ignore an action.

Ants seem to have a strong colony identity, the individual appearing to be of little significance. For humans there may well be a group identity that can sometimes take precedence, but usually a fair amount of individuality is apparent – one human brain operating in solo. When we come to look at intelligent machines in the next chapter, their link with ant intelligence may appear to be closer. It is the overall operation of a network of machines that is important and not so much the abilities of one individual machine.

SPIDER INTELLIGENCE

When we consider other inspects, such as spiders, the picture is no clearer. In fact, as more than 30,000 different species of spider are known to exist, each with vastly different characteristics, generalisations are not easy to make. Even so, a brief look at the way some spiders behave may help us understand more about the nature of intelligence.

In one Mexican species several individuals operate a web together, combining to tackle any relatively large prey which becomes trapped. Some crab-like spiders do not have a web, but live in a burrow with a trap-door entrance and rush out to grab any prey that ventures nearby. Some have even developed a range of trip wires – the prey stumbles and the spider pounces on it. Others (*Scytodidae*) hang around at night on walls and spit a venomous gum at their prey, the gum solidifying quickly on impact. This gum completely immobilises the prey which can be eaten when the spider is peckish.

Bolas spiders, found in Africa and North America, cling to a twig or leaf at night and dangle a length of silk. When an inspect passes near, the spider spins the sticky silk round to lasso it, then reels it in, in order to feed.

Water spiders live in ponds and lakes. They build an air-filled diving bell out of silk and wait, underwater, for passing prey such as shrimps or larvae. When prey is close the water spider pounces, shark-style, to deliver a fatal bite, returning to the lair to digest the prey. For this spider its lair is its life; it is where it rests, feeds, mates and lays eggs.

Many spiders, however, construct silky orb webs in bushes, buildings or close to the ground. Any insect which becomes attached to the web is stuck to it, whereupon the owner of the web rushes to the victim to deliver a paralysing blow. The spider tends to sit just above the centre of the web, presumably in order to minimise the time taken to get to its prey.

Spiders have a range of senses – chemical, vibratory, tactile and visual – and these all appear to come into play for sexual purposes. The strongest signal is perhaps the sexual pheromone in the threads of an adult female's web. Visual information exchanged between the male and female is important throughout. Subsequently, when in contact with each other, tactile signals are critical through leg play which appears to help prepare the female for copulation.

Female spiders of the *Dolomedes fribriatus* strain lure males, with their innate desire to mate, and promptly eat them when they get close. In order to minimise risk some 'clever' males bring along a present of prey which they place in the web. Only after the female has gorged herself will the male take its suit further. Likening this to the human male behaviour of buying chocolates or perfume for a woman would perhaps be flippant. So too would likening to human behaviour the activity of some male crab spiders, when they use a silky thread to tie down the female during the sexual act! Especially as the female (spider) is able to free herself quite easily afterwards.

In fact spiders are so different from humans that it is extremely difficult to make any comparisons at all, not only in terms of intelligence but regarding capabilities in general. Spiders differ greatly between types, with some curious extremes. Each spider's intelligence is obviously dependent on its physical characteristics and lifestyle, but one way in which all spiders are similar to each other, and even to humans, is that they produce offspring, the next link in the evolutionary chain. Undoubtedly this must be a primary goal for all organisms, as without it a species would simply die out. Can we therefore say that intelligence has something to do with the ability to produce offspring?

The ability to produce offspring might be assumed to be totally instinctive. Is this the case for you as a human? Or do/did you make some sort of selection? As with animal intelligence, it is difficult to decide how much of our behaviour is genetically programmed and how much is based on conscious thought. By means of each individual selecting a 'better' mate, a biological species evolves and gains strength. We could certainly argue therefore that the mental ability to selectively procreate is an implicit part of an individual's intelligence. This said, as in the case of bees, not all members of a species are able to procreate. This does not mean such members are unintelligent, but rather that they have a zero score in one dimension of their intelligence hypersphere.

BEE INTELLIGENCE

Having looked closely at ants and spiders, is there anything else we can deduce from other insects? One could easily fill several more volumes with the fascinating behaviour of insects but we only have time to look at one further important group, namely bees. Bees are particularly interesting because they have individual behavioural characteristics within a tightly knit society.

One notable feature of bees is their complex communication system. When a worker bee returns from an expedition to collect pollen and nectar, it performs a dance on the vertical surface of a comb in the hive. The dance takes the form of a repetitive sequence, firstly waggling the body as it moves forwards in a straight line, then circling back to the right, forwards in a straight line again, and finally circling back to the left. The distance of the straight line waggle is directly proportional to the distance of the source of pollen and nectar from the hive, while the angle of the straight run indicates the angle between the source and the sun. The translation of this geographically scaled information by the other bees in the hive appears to be amazingly accurate. Given the relatively small size of a bee's brain, compared to that of a human, such feats are astounding. They mean that bees have the ability to calculate proportions, relate abstract figures to their real-world counterparts and evaluate Pythagorean-type equations every time they head out from their hive to a food source.

Bees are able to adapt their flying behaviour depending on their environment, particularly in terms of the sun's position. They can travel distances of 10 kilometres or more, from their hive, in search of a food source. To achieve this, they use environmental features to gauge distance and direction.

It is incredible that a bee can find its way to a target by following a set of markers, not actually seeing the target until it gets there. This requires it to remember a number of routes. Research[5] has, however, indicated that bees do appear to be restricted to routes with distinct landmarks. They do not seem to be able to relate one route to another and get into all sorts of problems when a landmark is moved or dramatically altered in some way. Despite this, they can quickly re-orientate themselves as soon as they spot a familiar landmark, even if they approach the landmark from a different direction. If the position of a hive or nest is changed, yet remains within the bee's normal flying zone, the bee can quickly adapt and still use familiar landmarks, despite a different frame of reference for its home base.

Many creatures, particularly bees, are able to relate the sun's movement across the sky, to landmarks. In this way bees are able to employ a natural clock on a daily basis, resorting to partial dead reckoning when thick cloud cover occurs, information being passed on via the communication dance. Interestingly, it appears that a bee's innate sense of the sun's movement through the sky is only an initial rough guess, which becomes much more accurate as they learn their own local geography through flight experience.

A number of experiments have been carried out to test the significance of the sun's movement for the flight geography of bees.[6] In one study a hive situated just south of the equator was moved into the northern hemisphere. The foraging bees found it extremely difficult to return home in their first few flights, and a large number failed to do so, apparently compensating incorrectly for the sun's movement. While even the most experienced bees can get tricked in such an experiment, for first-time foragers, who have yet to orient themselves, it is estimated that approximately one in five fail to return from their first trip out. This loss rate drops to zero after very few trips. Hence it appears that the geography/sun learning phase is critical. Without such learning bees would only be able to exist in one hive in one location, clearly not a desirable feature for the species as a whole.

In another research project[7] bees were placed in a hive inside an artificially lit area in which the lighting remained in a fixed position. When the hive was subsequently placed outside, the foraging bees immediately got lost – apparently confused by the sun's moving light.

In contrast, the weather-predicting capabilities of bees do seem to be innate rather than learnt. When a serious storm approaches, any bees foraging a long distance from the hive do not, on their return, attempt to recruit other bees by doing the communication dance. Those foraging closer to home continue to do so, however. The maximum distance for recruitment seems to be determined by the expected severity of the storm.

The time clock in a bee is accurate. We know this from experiments in which a food source has been made available at certain times of the day. The bees rapidly learn the exact times that the food will be available and return there regularly, just before 'opening time'. After about one week the food source is removed. The same bees still turn up at the same time every day and stay for several minutes, before giving up. Next day they are back again, giving the impression that once something is learnt it is difficult for a bee to forget it. How much does this resemble human behaviour? It certainly brings to mind the expression 'You can't teach an old dog new tricks.'

BEE SENSES

In general a bee's vision is poor and it needs to fly within a few metres of a landmark in order to recognise it. However, bees have been shown experimentally to have colour vision. By placing a food source on a card of a particular colour, amongst cards of different colours, bees can be trained to return to that particular colour even when the card positions are altered and no food source is present. Unlike humans, bees can also recognise ultraviolet light, as indeed can machines.

A bee's brain is about 0.01 per cent of the size of a human brain, in terms of cells and connections. Yet its brain has to cope with about 2 per cent of the sensory information that the human brain receives. This means that, for every fifty sensory connections to the human brain, a bee has one, whereas for every 10,000 brain cells in a human, a bee has one. This means that a bee's brain is proportionally much richer in sensory input than is the human brain.

In terms of hearing, a bee's brain is tuned to certain frequencies. Bees do not have human-like ears covering a broad sound range but they do have a set of sound sensors on their legs which pick up vibrated messages. They also have sound sensors on their antennae. These pick up communicated signals from the information dance, one set being tuned in at around 20 Hz, whilst the others are tuned in between 250 Hz and 300 Hz.[8] Having such finely tuned hearing means that signals at other frequencies, such as buzzing in the hive, are not picked up at all. To put this in perspective, a typical human's hearing is reasonable from 0 to about 15,000 Hz. Most human speech, however, occurs between 300 and 3,400 Hz (the range of a normal telephone). Machines, of course, have much broader, more powerful communicating abilities, no such limit of 15,000 Hz applying at all.

A bee's nose is an extremely important organ. Its refined smelling capabilities are at least as good as those of a well-trained human. Not only that but bees can smell substances such as carbon dioxide and water vapour, which are undetectable by humans. Like us, bees can learn to recognise thousands of different aromas. However, some odours have a special meaning, and there are a number of receptors which respond to specific smells. These smells include the odour from decaying dead bees, which need to be removed from the hive. Although most bees die on foraging expeditions, in a busy hive as many as 100 bees may die each day and their bodies need to be cleared out.

Other important odours are those the queen sends out to attract nurse bees, others to stop the production of new queens and even some to stop the workers from laying eggs. Workers themselves give off banana-scented alarm pheromones to indicate anger, attracting co-workers to their side, ready to sting anything that moves. Another worker pheromone can indicate a good food source, attracting bees who are down wind. One interesting use of odour is the Nasinov gland pheromone with which the bees mark the hive as an aid to those who are returning.[9] When strong winds occur foraging bees land and wait until the wind subsides. On returning, they use their wings to fan their Nasinov gland at the hive entrance as a signal to others.

COMPARING INTELLIGENCES

An intriguing characteristic of bees is the technique they have of recruiting other bees, by means of their communicating dance, when they feel they have found a good food source. This is very much a form of advertising – persuading others that you have information about something they will like.

The more we study insects, the more we realise just how intelligent they are in their own way. Much of the complexity of their lives is still not known. What exactly is going on in their brains? Do they have abstract thoughts? Unfortunately we simply cannot tell. What we can see is that insects clearly learn and adapt and these are critical aspects of intelligence.

For each insect its capabilities depend on its physical make-up, its sensors and its actuators. The world exists for an individual in terms of how that individual perceives its environment and interacts with it. This is true of insects and animals, just as it is of humans. An individual's intelligence depends directly on its perception.

Nowadays, however, we also have machines: robots with computers for brains, for decision-making. Such machines can act as a collective. How does the intelligence of a machine compare with that of an insect or even with that of a human? In the next chapter we will investigate what it means for a machine to be intelligent and how a machine's intellectual capabilities compare with what we've already seen.

One key point is that a bee has 10,000 brain cells, dogs and cats typically have 1000 times that number, and humans 10,000 times more than that. We can draw some loose parallels between brain size (in terms of cells and connections) and abilities. How does this stand up when we look at machines?

12

MACHINE
INTELLIGENCE

—

A TYPICAL, FULLY FUNCTIONING ADULT human brain consists of something like 100 billion neurons, each one of which is, on average, connected to approximately 10,000 others. These neurons vary in their structure depending on their position in the brain. For example, those near the optic nerve, feeding in visual information, are different from those which control movement, the motor neurons. The number and make-up of neurons present within a brain is species-dependent. For example, a sea slug has eight or nine neurons, which are larger than any human neuron, but which, due to their number, are connected together in a simpler way. A frog, meanwhile, has several million neurons concerned solely with its vision processes, and these cells have a complexity which is not matched by human neurons. When comparing human neurons with those of other creatures, the main difference is not that human neurons are bigger or more complex, but quite simply that there are a lot more of them and they are more highly connected.

So how does computer processing stand in comparison? Human and other animal neurons are biological, carbon-based; whereas computers are typically constructed out of silicon. It is therefore difficult to make a direct comparison because the basic processing units are composed of different materials. Also, whilst the number of human neurons remains relatively steady from generation to generation, with only a slight evolutionary pull, computer processing power is increasing rapidly. At present, a single computer in Japan[1] consists of approximately 10 million cells. The system is based on cellular automata, in that each neuron has its own automatic action, like a brain cell. The manufacturers claim that the computer has processing capabilities roughly equal to those of a cat. Although, as we have said, it is almost impossible to make a direct comparison, a typical personal computer of today has perhaps the equivalent of tens of thousands of cells – rather more than a bee.

Whereas a human brain operates mainly in stand-alone fashion, within a human body, most computer systems are connected into a network and it is the combined processing capabilities of the network that are important. Even without networking, if the present rate of increase continues, computers with, roughly speaking, the same processing capabilities as humans will exist within the next decade. By 2020 computers will be far more powerful. It would take a major reversal in technological advance for this not to occur.

INHERENT AND RESULTANT INTELLIGENCE

Processing capabilities, whether in terms of human brain cells, the insect form or the machine form, only provide an inherent intelligence capability. With no connections to the outside world a brain could neither perceive the world nor have any effect on it. Effective brain power, with its associated intelligence, is realised when a brain can sense the world, thereby perceiving it, and as a result, act upon it. This 'resultant' intelligence is what actually has an effect on the world and is what can be measured in various ways.

When one human considers the intelligence of another human it is only their resultant intelligence that is under scrutiny. With machines it is the same. To have a resultant intelligence, a computer needs to be able to sense the world in some way and then have the ability to carry out physical actions, or to cause physical actions to be carried out.

What, though, does it mean for a machine to be intelligent? In considering this question, we must look at a machine as an individual, with its own abilities. Just as we might treat a bee or spider with a degree of respect for what it can do, so we should treat a machine. Its brain may be composed of different matter but that does not mean we should conclude that it is unintelligent. Just because a machine cannot do something that a particular human can do, or perhaps can-not do it in exactly the same way, we should not assume that it is therefore inferior in *all* aspects to all humans.[2] This would indeed be folly.

MACHINE LEARNING AND ADAPTATION

In common with other animals and insects, human intelligence appears to be partly due to nature and partly nurture (that is partly genetically programed and partly due to learning and experience). Many machines are simply programed, both physically and mentally. In other words, they will continue to do the same physical thing in the same controlled way; they do not learn or adapt their behaviour. Indeed many simple machines, such as kettles, toasters or ticket dispensers, are employed for exactly this reason. They do jobs that humans could do, but they have a number of distinct advantages due to their accuracy and speed.

Nowadays, however, there are increasing numbers of machines that can adapt their behaviour based on what they have learnt. They are physically constructed and have an initial program – the hardware and software easily being put together by humans. These machines or robots offer us the opportunity to investigate intelligence on an individual machine basis.

Robots have the potential to sense the world in a much broader way than humans: to include, for example, ultraviolet, infrared, radar and ultrasonics, as well as vision, touch and so on. To a robot which is sensing in terms of ultraviolet and infrared, the world appears very different from the world as perceived by a robot with other sensors.

One big difference between humans and machines is that all humans are equipped with roughly the same set of sensors, although with some people they may not function correctly. Machines, however, can vary from microwaves to automobiles, each with their own very different capabilities. If one human can achieve a feat, it is straightforward to conclude that other humans will probably be able to achieve the same result. With machines it is impossible to say that because one machine does something, all machines can do it; or that because one machine cannot do something, no machine can do that thing. It would clearly be foolish to draw conclusions about intelligent robots based on what a toaster can or cannot do.[3]

Examples of both successful and unsuccessful experimentation occur frequently within the Cybernetics Department at Reading University. For instance, in October 1997 a robot called R.O.G.E.R.R. was entered in the Great Sam Half Marathon at Bracknell. I ran in front of R.O.G.E.R.R. with an infrared transmitter attached to a bum bag around my waist.

R.O.G.E.R.R., whose infrared receiver picked up my signals, was programed to follow 2 metres behind me, speeding up, slowing down and turning left or right accordingly. We had designed R.O.G.E.R.R. to ensure that no rain got into his electronics and even gave him a peaked cap to keep the sun out.

On the day of the race the sun was very bright and low in the sky. The sun is perhaps the most powerful natural source of infrared available, and was certainly a lot more powerful than my bum bag transmitter. Although R.O.G.E.R.R. initially followed me, he soon caught sight of the sun and headed towards it, trying to get 2 metres away. Unfortunately he crashed into the kerb and, instead of becoming the first robot in the world to successfully complete a half marathon, he became the first with an athletic injury.

The clear lesson to be learnt from this experiment is that robots sense the world in a different way from humans. How similar was R.O.G.E.R.R. to the bees who could not cope when their hive was moved or the ants which marched in the opposite direction from the sun?

We also have a troupe of robots at Reading called the Seven Dwarfs, which have ultrasonic 'eyes' on their insect-like faces. By means of a microprocessor brain, these robots are used to investigate learning. Once switched on, they are on their own in a little corral, about 2 metres in diameter. Their goal in life is 'to move forwards but never hit anything', and each robot has to learn what to do with its two wheels (right and left) in order to achieve that aim. The ultrasonic sensors tell the robot what situation it is in (for example, something is close on the left). By a process of trial and error, the robot has to learn what is a good thing to do with its wheels in order to achieve its goal. In the situation mentioned, perhaps moving its left wheel forwards, for a few seconds, and its right wheel backwards will do the trick.

After a while the robot gets around fairly well, occasionally making a mistake and hitting the wall. Each time it is switched on, however, it is effectively a new robot, ending up with particular habits and characteristics that it has learnt. When it does something well with its wheels it is rewarded (the weightings in its microprocessor brain associated with that action are strengthened), whereas when it does something badly it is punished and the converse takes place. The resultant robot is an individual, behaving in a way that it has learnt to behave, partly due to its inbuilt program and partly due to its experience.

In May 1998, when demonstrating the learning technique at Uppingham School, we varied the experiment slightly: each time the robot moved something was placed in its way. When it turned right or left it was told that was wrong. In the end the robot gave up completely and just quivered near the middle of the corral, yet the robot was still fully operative. It had decided that, because whatever it did was wrong, it was not going to do anything, even though this was contrary to its goal in life.

Earlier, in November 1996, one of our robots learnt how to move around in the corral at Reading University while connected, via a radio link, to the internet. Once it had finished learning, without human intervention, it programed another one of our robots, via the internet, to behave in the same way, the other robot being situated at the State University of New York at Buffalo, USA. This experiment, which aimed to show that robots can program each other with what they have learnt themselves, appears in the 1999 *Guinness Book of Records*.

Other similar robots have a ring of infrared communicators, worn like a crown on their heads; with these they signal to each other to indicate who and where they are. Each robot can detect where the other robots are, and is aware of which robot is where. The robots can flock together, rather like sheep, simply by heading towards the greatest concentration of signalling robots. Any robot can decide, in one of a number of ways, to be a leader, and head off in a particular direction with the other robots following behind. Clearly, communication, interaction and adaptive collective behaviours between robots are all important aspects of their intelligence.

Innate programed behaviours and capabilities help to define any species, but real progress is made when individuals within that species learn, and adapt their behaviour. For this reason, mutual learning (with up to four robots signalling to each other) has been investigated. In these experiments each robot passes on its experiences to the others, thus speeding up the learning process.

A recently completed project involved two robots, a 'parent' and 'child'. The parent selected a particular signal to describe a situation it was in. The child could then associate the situations it got into with the signals from its parent. Further signals indicated the actions to be taken in each situation. In this way the robots created their own language, which was used between them, to describe their world and actions taken in it. The language could quite easily have been expanded to describe particular features or places in the robots' world or even for game-playing between the robots.

If we compare this type of signalling and learning with the communication dances of the bees discussed in Chapter 11 we can see that, while the bee signals appear to be largely innate, with little learning involved, the robot signals are more complex. In fact if we leave them for a while to sort themselves out, the signalling which occurs between the robots is very difficult to decipher even when we know, roughly speaking, what to look for.

If the robots existed in a more complex environment that humans were not fully aware of, it would be impossible for humans to understand what the robots were saying to each other, particularly if the robots were investigating the world by means of radar, ultraviolet or other senses of which we were unaware. When we consider other species, we only understand a small part of what is going on in their lives. We have little idea what they are communicating to each other and why.

With robots we can look at their resultant intelligence – how they sense the world and how they respond to their senses. Even then it is difficult to know what they are thinking at any time and why they have carried out a specific action, particularly if it seems, to us, to be illogical. This is the phenomenon of 'Artificial Life', an apt description of some machines which can appear to be alive in a similar way to biological creatures.

It can be very difficult for humans to decide if a robot is alive or not. For instance, in November 1999, I, along with Iain Goodhew (another member of the team), took a number of robots on a tour of Russia. These included some of the Seven Dwarfs just described, Elma a six-legged robot, and Hissing Sid a large robot cat. Hissing Sid is approximately the size of a small tiger. Because of this size and his complexity, British Airways were asked if Sid could have a seat on the plane from London to Moscow. The reply was 'Sorry, no, because British Airways does not allow animals in the cabin.' In all fairness British Airways later changed their minds and Sid was able to stretch out on three free seats, on both the outward and home-bound journeys.

Is Machine Intelligence Real?

Although Alan Turing may not have wished it, his name will forever be associated with the Turing Test, which can be described briefly as – 'A human judge holds a three-way computer communication with a computer and another human, both of whom are unseen. If the judge cannot distinguish between the responses of the human and the computer, then the computer passes the test.'[4] At present, it is not felt that any computer is close to passing the test. But this is not surprising, as it is all about mimicking human behaviour in linguistic communication, with all its subtle nuances and witticisms.

The test is based on the assumption that the ability to engage in human communication indicates the existence of a high level of intelligence. My guess is that, as soon as a machine does pass the test, we will hear many voices saying, 'Well we knew all along that the Turing Test wasn't really an indication of intelligence, and now a machine has passed the test we have been proved correct.' We will probably also be told that, 'Because of the number of finite words in any language, such a test is actually playing on some of the advantages of machines.'

At Reading we are not so interested in the Turing Test. Instead, we wish to look at the intelligence of robots in their own right, asking how they learn and communicate, and how they cope with contradictory information from different sensors. Artificial Intelligence is not about getting machines to copy what we do, but rather, exploring how machines do what *they* do, and think the way *they* think. Machines do, however, have a number of advantages over humans, when it comes to their intelligence – their ability to deal with a wider range of sensory information being one of them.

The fact that machine intelligence is so different from human intelligence means we must be careful about what conclusions we draw, and learn some lessons from the past. For example, many years ago it was believed that neither humans nor machines would ever be able to fly. In 1895 the eminent scientist, Lord Kelvin, said, 'Heavier-than-air-flying machines are not possible.' Five years later Simon Newcomb, a well-respected US astronomer, proved mathematically than it was not possible for such machines to fly. In 1903, however, Wilbur and Orville Wright took to the air at Kitty Hawk, North Carolina. Amazingly, Newcomb stuck to his theory that manned flight was not possible, for several more years, illustrating the general human difficulty in thinking outside our present frame of reference. Machines fly in a different way from birds, achieving much greater speeds and heights. We should therefore try to avoid falling into the same trap of making wild claims about the so-called inferiority of machine intelligence, just because our own present, human way of thinking is limited.

Yet many such claims are currently being made. It is said that humans are intelligent in a special way, machines will never be intelligent in the same way, therefore machines will always be less intelligent than humans and will remain subservient to humans. One person who subscribes to this view is Sir Roger Penrose, Rouse Ball Professor of Mathematics at Oxford University. In 1994 he wrote, 'Computers would always remain subservient to us, no matter how far they advance with respect to speed, capacity and logical design.'[5]

Just as Newcomb could mathematically prove something to be impossible, that was in fact possible, so various philosophical confidence tricksters have done the same thing in recent times with intelligence. One famous example of this is John Searle's Chinese Room Problem.[6] He used the example of a man sitting in a room containing Chinese symbols. Certain Chinese symbols are passed to the man. Although he does not understand Chinese he can pass back other Chinese symbols because he follows the instructions in a rule book. The argument is that a computer does nothing more than carry out programmed instructions.

Yet we know that machines are not all simply programed; some of them do have the ability to learn. Not only that but machines tend to communicate in a language suitable for machines, not a human language such as Chinese or English. Expecting them to communicate in a human language would be as biased as expecting humans to respond efficiently to parallel infrared signalling! But the Chinese Room is merely one discussion piece which can be clearly seen to be biased.[7] Another philosophical hot potato is the phenomenon of consciousness.

THE CONSCIOUSNESS PROBLEM

I believe that dogs and cats are conscious, in their own way, and bees, ants and spiders are conscious, not as humans but as bees, ants and spiders. Even sea slugs, with eight or nine brain cells are conscious, in their way. I do not feel in a position to say that, as a human, I am conscious, but other creatures – such as slugs, wasps and dogs – are not like me, therefore they are not conscious. I cannot say that a robot, with a computer for a brain, is not conscious, because its brain is not like mine and because it thinks in a different way to me. Presumably a robot can be conscious, but in a robot way. Just as it is difficult to know what it is like to be a bat, when you are not a bat, so it is difficult to know what it is like to be a robot, when you are not a robot.

Many different theories exist, attempting to explain the exact nature of consciousness. Some theorists point to mystical physical properties of the human brain, perhaps caused by quantum effects, that we do not yet understand.[8] Penrose says, 'There are external manifestations of conscious objects (brains) that differ from the external manifestations of a computer ... such non-computational action would have to be found in an area of physics that lies outside the presently known physical laws.' Searle, meanwhile, writes, 'Once you have described the facts about my body and brain, you still seem to have a lot of facts left over about my beliefs, desires, pains, etc.'

Others indicate that a full comprehension of the situation will always be beyond the reach of science. For example, the Nobel Laureate Sir John Eccles believes that 'God attaches the soul to the unborn foetus at the age of about three weeks.'[9] Unfortunately this is reminiscent of the fanaticism that years ago fought against evolutionary theory. The storyline appears to go: we want something to be true (in this case human superiority), so we will remain stone deaf to scientific evidence and thinking, and come up with an argument based largely on hocus-pocus and magic. To borrow the words of Clarence Darrow,[10] who in 1925 was the defence lawyer for John Scopes who had been charged with teaching evolution in school, if we bow to those who place human consciousness as a fundamental requirement for intelligence, 'we are marching backwards to the glorious age of the sixteenth century when bigots lighted faggots to burn men who dared to bring any intelligence and enlightenment and culture to the human mind.'

It is evident that humans are intelligent in their own way, something which depends on our physical make-up as well as how our brains operate. As we have seen in the last two chapters, other creatures are intelligent in their own ways, again dependent on their physical make-up and the operation of their brains. In each case, even with humans, it is very difficult to know how much intelligent behaviour is due to genetic programing and how much to learning.

With machines things are different again. There are many distinct forms of machine, some very simple, some very complex. Their physical sizes differ enormously, their power capabilities vary considerably, and their intellectual capabilities exhibit perhaps the biggest variation of all. Just as different creatures have different abilities and are perhaps intelligent in different ways, the same is true of machines.

Consciousness, in any being, is an abstract entity and is certainly not the easiest thing to pin down. It is virtually impossible to find out whether one person has more or less consciousness than someone else. And, because of the fact that it cannot be measured, consciousness is prime philosophical fodder. With intelligence in an individual, however, we are really looking at how that person responds to stimuli and how they affect the world, i.e. their resultant intelligence. Though this is something that can be measured and compared, it is more a case of what exactly do we measure, and how do we compare.

HUMANS VERSUS MACHINES

Our present understanding of the human brain's operation is certainly limited. However, recent research on machine intelligence, in terms of characteristics such as memory, learning, decision-making and behavioural responses, not only raises questions as to the nature of machine intelligence but also alters our view of exactly what human intelligence is.

As we saw earlier, tests of human intelligence in this century have often been based on questions involving memory (i.e. recalling facts) and numerical mathematics (i.e. calculating or sequencing numbers). Years ago, some people earned a good living by memorising huge numbers of facts and toured the world showing what geniuses they were. The same was true of individuals who showed incredible prowess with number manipulation. Yet now we know that the average computer is far superior to humans in these areas. In the time it takes a typical human to get a numerical problem wrong, a typical computer may well have calculated a billion, or more, similar questions correctly. So, do these achievements give any indication at all of intelligence? If so, some machines have already outstripped humans in these particular areas. Conversely, if they do not give any indication of intelligence, why do we keep testing students on these skills in school and university exams and IQ tests? Machine intelligence is making us think again about human intelligence.

Of the key pointers to intelligence perhaps the most prominent, apart from the Turing Test, has traditionally been held to be the game of chess. Once machines could beat humans at chess, it was argued, they would be truly intelligent (particularly as chess is defined in *The Macmillan Encyclopaedia* (1995) as a science, an art, involving tactics and strategy and a psychological simulation of war requiring ingenuity and pure skill). In May 1997, it happened. The human world chess champion, Gary Kasparov, was beaten in a six-game series by IBM's chess-playing computer, Deep Blue.

At the time Gary complained of all sorts of cheating going on (presumably mainly by the computer), and when I met up with him in the summer of 1999 the defeat still rankled. Whether Kasparov had a bad day, and made an uncharacteristic error, is neither here nor there. The fact is that the computer won. I heard one comment shortly afterwards to the effect that Kasparov knew he was playing chess, whereas the computer did not. This comment typifies the human bias that must be removed if we are to gain a true understanding of intelligence, not only in different creatures and machines, but also in humans. What is important, as with all aspects of intelligence, is what results have been achieved. On a similar test a machine, an ant, a dog and a human may all tackle things in different ways (so too may different humans). What if Hans, the horse, mentioned earlier, had been taught to play chess? Surely we would think him an intelligent horse. What if Hans then beat the human world champion?

A game such as chess provides a balanced test. If two humans play each other, the best person wins. If a human plays a machine then the best individual wins. Other factors, like the weather, money and influence, are reduced to a minimum or removed altogether. The same is true of other games of this type. In the game of draughts, for instance, computers have been beating humans for some time. More recently the same has become true of backgammon. Now other games, such as bridge and go, are being brought into the arena. But are these any real test of machine intelligence?

Deep Blue had almost 500 microprocessors, all specifically aimed at the problem of chess, enabling the computer to look at something like two million chess positions every second, and thereby search for the best strategic position in a very short time. So essentially, a 'suck it and see' approach was taken, the main advantages for Deep Blue being its speed and accuracy. Meanwhile, Kasparov presumably used some type of pattern matching associated with a logically operating memory.

So far computer systems that have been put together for the purposes of chess, with the aim of following human thought processing more closely, have not done quite so well. It may well be that its biological base makes the human brain good at doing what it does, just as its silicon base does the same for a computer.

For computers, and humans, chess, backgammon and draughts all have the advantage that complete information on the state of the game can be witnessed as it stands. No unknown factors occur. However, with games such as bridge or poker, the information on other hands in the game is imperfect. Early attempts with computers tended to model the way humans approach these games. But the more common approach now, which relies on the available processing power, is to run through a whole series of possibilities in which each opponent has been dealt a random hand. The best play is then selected, based on the one which came out best given the range of hands tested. The computer can take on a 'safety first' approach, playing the percentages, or 'go for broke' with a riskier strategy.

For the most part, computers attempting to copy a human brain's approach to games have not proved to be good enough to beat the human best. But with backgammon this is no longer so, as an artificial neural (brain) network has proved successful. The network is made up of computer-based versions of simple neurons, connected with some complexity. And it looks as though, within the next few years, the situation will be much the same with bridge.

The Future of Machine Intelligence

It has been said that humans tend to look at a problem and make direct associations in a relatively parallel way. Conversely, the computers that have proved to be successful at the game challenges tend to operate in more of a serial way, testing one possibility after the other. Whilst this may well be the usual case at the moment, there is no reason why it should remain so.

Speed of operation is a distinct advantage of computers over the much slower, human brain. This differential will increase further in the years ahead, as computers get faster and acquire greater memory capabilities. With this in mind we need to be aware that, whilst biological evolution (including humans and their associated intelligence) is a slow process, machine evolution (including computers and their associated intelligence) is rapid. A machine can be designed, yet in a few seconds a much improved, more intelligent machine can be evolved and constructed. The next version (generation) of a machine can be so much improved as to make the initial model almost unrecognisable. While human intelligence will slowly plod forward into the future, machine intelligence will evolve rapidly. It is humans who have set this trend in motion, but it is machines that are now designing and evolving more powerful machines.

Another clear advantage of machine intelligence is its ability to deal with information in many dimensions. The human brain has evolved, within the human body, to deal with two- or three-dimensional information, and sometimes only one-dimensional information (as in the case of IQ test results). Humans attempt to simplify everything down to these levels. There is nothing inherently wrong with this for humans; indeed it has been a critical factor in our success. Computers, however, can deal with many variables at the same time, and investigate the complex relationships that exist.

As time goes by we are deferring to machines and relying on their decisions more and more, particularly when it comes to complex problems. My own experience with one of the supermarket chains in the UK has involved dealing with the regular purchasing habits of approximately 50,000 customers, related to 100 product types. The problem is a multi-dimensional one and is thus very difficult for humans to comprehend, but easy for computers. For instance, if a customer defects to a competing store this is not good for the supermarket; it is in their interest to do all they can to hold on to the customer. But are there any indicative signs, in their purchasing habits, before they defect? For a particular type of person it may be that if they stop buying milk this is a clear sign. So the supermarket can offer that individual free milk in order to hold on to their trade. There are huge complexities involving different people and their buying habits and such indicators can only be detected by computers.

It is extraordinary to think how much we now rely on machines as part of our everyday lives. Could we, in the Western world, actually live a day without having contact with a machine? Think about it. Where does your water come from? What about your communications? What about money? Any rational prediction of the future indicates that this reliance on machines, particularly to do our thinking and decision-making for us, will increase. In 1999 we witnessed a group of people living entirely from the worldwide web, with no direct interaction with other humans outside their group. All food and consumables, and many luxuries, were arranged in comfort. We also saw on BBC1 in 1998, the construction of a 'Dream House', a networked house in which food was automatically ordered to replenish the fridge, and all aspects of the house's functioning were arranged by the computer.

In the Western world humans have undeniably created a technologically based society that functions with computers and machines at its core. Humans evolved to cope well as hunter-gatherers, yet in a short space of time we have created a society that not only thrives on information but depends on it as its lifeblood.

Human intelligence has great difficulty in coping with this new environment. Quite simply, far too much information exists for us to even remotely hope to grapple with. It is computers that are really suited to this information age, with their ability to think in many dimensions and deal with many variables and inputs. Human intelligence evolved in a world which no longer exists. How can we possibly conceive in twenty or thirty dimensions? How can we survive in a world to which we are not as well adapted as our creations?

One possibility, as suggested by a number of science fiction writers[11] as well as scientists, is to link humans and technology together even more closely, via a physical and mental connection. This might be through the unravelling of DNA molecules, allowing computers to be constructed from living DNA. Or it might be through actual hard-wiring of humans to machines. What are called 'wearable computers' (tiny computers that augment clothes, shoes or wrist-watches) go some way towards this. The interface between human thought processes and actions, and the computer technology is, however, still relatively slow and remote. What is much more useful is the use of implant technology, thereby inextricably coupling humans and machines together.

13

A CYBORG
FUTURE?

—

IN MANY CASES PHYSICALLY STRONGER humans are 'used' by
other humans who are themselves in a controlling position either
because of birth into the 'right' family, or more likely because they
are intellectually more capable. Machines have been created either to
do things humans do not want to do or because they can out-perform humans due to their strength or speed. This works well when
the machine is programed or has little or nothing that could be con-
strued as intelligence.

Nowadays, however, machines such as robots (with computers
for brains) raise serious questions as to whether humans can continue
to be in control of all machines in the future. If a machine can out-
think a human, and is allowed to do something about it, then a rather
different picture emerges.

Looking at the human hypersphere of intelligence, one can argue about which aspects of intelligence should really be considered useful and which not. If we chose only those aspects which were important for life and human domination over other species, then what would happen if a machine could easily out-perform humans on most of these aspects? In other words, what would happen if a machine had a hypersphere with a larger area? Would this not allow the machine to at least question why it was doing certain things for a human, a being less intelligent than itself?

It could be argued that, no matter how intelligent the machine, as long as there is a human in control, who can switch it on or off, they will stay in control. (I suppose this would work something like human slavery used to in days gone by.) But think again. Even now, would it be possible to switch off the internet – perhaps the most powerful of present-day mechanical entities? Conversely, can we assume that machines of the future, which will be far more intelligent than humans, will be content to be controlled by us? I think not.

It is difficult to conceive of any aspect of human intelligence in which machines either cannot or will not be able to out-perform humans.[1] With brains that operate much faster than ours, that take in sensory information that we cannot, and think in dimensions that are way beyond us, how can humans possibly hope to stay in control? This is naivety indeed. But could there be any mileage in the old adage 'if you can't beat them join them'?

TOWARDS A CYBORG FUTURE

In August 1998 I had a silicon chip transponder surgically implanted into my left arm. As I entered the main door to the Cybernetics Department at Reading University, a radio frequency signal, across the doorway, excited the coil in the transponder, providing current to the silicon chip circuitry, allowing for the repetitive transfer of 64 bits of information. The building's computer was able to recognise me from the unique signal transmitted from my implant. So it welcomed me by saying 'Hello Professor Warwick', it switched on the foyer light for me and selected my web page on the video screen.

Elsewhere in the building, as I approached my laboratory the door opened automatically, allowing me to pass freely. The computer kept a record of when I entered the building, when I left, which room I was in and when I got there. While such an experiment indicates some of the possibilities of what are becoming widely known as 'intelligent' buildings, it also marks a veritable enhancement of the capabilities of the human body.

Since then a research team at Emory University in Atlanta has implanted a similar transmitting device in the brain of a stroke patient, linking up human brain cells, neurons, with the silicon chips present. In this way brain motor signals have been transmitted directly to a computer, allowing the patient to learn how to move the cursor around on a computer screen using brain signals alone. Meanwhile a group in Maine have been able to send signals from a computer to the nervous system of a man with a broken spinal cord to control his physical activity.

Human nervous system signals can be transmitted to, and received from, a computer, via an implant making use of radio signalling. Not only does this mean that such signalling can bypass computer keyboards, but enhancing the human brain in this way may also give us a window of time in which to keep pace with technological change. It means that movements, emotions and even thoughts may be transmittable to computers and, via the internet, to other humans with similar implants.[2] The technical possibility therefore exists to send a signal from your own nervous system, perhaps when you are feeling angry, via the internet, down onto the nervous system of another person. What will they feel when they receive your 'anger' signals? Will they feel angry like you? Clearly, sending electronic signals directly from one person's brain to another has a lot of unknowns attached. But it also offers extraordinary opportunities.

These technological developments will also mean that signals can be sent from machine to human brain. For example, engineers at Siemens Roke Manor Research laboratories in the UK are envisaging the possibility of implanting cameras into the eyes of journalists. TV news will apparently undergo a complete transformation as live images are transmitted directly from sensors attached to a reporter's optic nerve. Admitting that the technology to achieve this is essentially already available, the chief technical officer at Roke Manor, Ian Stewart, talks of a ten-year timescale for implementation. Sensory information, such as x-rays or ultraviolet signals, can similarly be fed in directly to the brain to enhance the normal range of human senses.

Extra memory and further mathematical abilities may also be connected in via the same route. Linking silicon up with the human nervous system and brain in this way will clearly change the way we interact with the world, and the way we think. What will the word 'I' mean if human and machine are permanently linked together? And what sort of intelligence will we have when human and machine brains are connected as one overall entity, part silicon, part carbon?

It seems that we may well see a different type of human emerge in the future, one who is inextricably linked to technology. The electronic signals from a human brain will connect directly with the electronic signals from a machine (computer) brain. Once again, a pretty rapid form of evolution will take place. We, or at least some of us, will go through a technical evolution, as we become, to all intents and purposes, cyborgs – part human, part machine.[4]

If we continue to use the machinery we have at present then the interface necessary will take a different form. For instance, we would no longer need a steering wheel in order to drive a car. We could get it to turn left or right and speed up or down, just by thinking about it. And how would the human brain respond to ultrasonic or ultraviolet information being fed directly into it? Clearly, there may need to be some adjustment of the human/cyborg brain to cope with all the different types of information it receives. Multi-dimensional thought, mathematics and memory could all be taken care of by the machine part, whereas the human part would have to get used to sensory information of another kind. We would have what is now called extra-sensory perception, even telepathy, between humans.

NETWORK INTELLIGENCE

It must be remembered, however, that a computer will more than likely be connected to a network. When a human is connected, via an implant, to such a computer they are therefore effectively connected to the network. In particular, when a human brain is connected to a computer brain, the intelligence of the network (with both human and machine nodes or 'points' of connection), exploits both machine and human intelligence.

At present, though, it remains very difficult for us to get to grips, both physically and mentally, with the machine world. Elma, one of our six-legged walking robots, can be compared to insects or animals because it moves around like them and looks something like them. However, its computer brain and nervous system are exactly the same as those used in the 'intelligent' building (that is, the Department of Cybernetics at Reading University). From an 'intelligence' point of view, Elma and the building have roughly the same characteristics. But how can we hope to compare the intelligence of such a building with human intelligence?

If we look at the intelligence of a single robot or computer we can see even now that there are a number of ways in which such entities out-perform the best that humans have to offer. As technology advances, the range of their capabilities will increase rapidly, particularly in the business and military sectors where immediate returns on investments can be gained. It is in fact difficult to think of any area of human intelligence (even including that intelligence solely associated with being human) in which a machine will not soon be able to out-perform us. Such conclusions immediately raise concerns about the long-term survival of humans.[5]

Perhaps, though, we should take another view. Rather than considering the intelligence of individual beings, whether human, insect or computer, we should look to the operation of a bee hive, where one can ask if the hive is itself intelligent. Here, however, we are looking at networks, connecting machines and humans. Each machine and human performs a role as part of the network. The intelligence in question is therefore the collective network intelligence.

When we apply the Theory of Subjective Intelligence the picture becomes clear: the role of a network is defined by its particular area of operation. This may be as a military network or perhaps as a business network. Its success or failure, and hence its intelligence, is thus measured in terms of its performance in its own field of operation. This involves the way it takes in information through its senses, how it responds innately, how it learns and adapts to changes, and how it makes and carries out decisions based on its overall frame of mind. The intelligence of the future is certainly the intelligence of networks. Let us hope that human intelligence is deemed by the machines running the network, to be worthy of being included as an important, integral part of the whole.

14

INTO THE
UNKNOWN

S O WHERE HAS OUR INVESTIGATION into intelligence taken us? Firstly, with humans we can see that the intelligence of an individual is as a result of their mental processes. It follows that what that individual regards as intelligence is also a result of their mental processes. Within a particular group what is regarded as intelligence is based on a general consensus, which naturally depends on the culture and values of that society. This, as we have seen, is very subjective to particular groupings.

In particular with humans, what an individual considers to be an intelligent act is very personal to them and depends on what skills and thought processes they value. These judgements are directly affected by their life, their culture and their own mental processes. In fact it has been said that, 'Any attempts to define intelligence that do not involve identifying specially valued cultural attainments must fail.'[1] In essence, intelligence in individuals is a function of the society in which they exist.

Out of the context of a society, intelligence is, by and large, meaningless. Any measurements or value judgements must be made with regard to a culture and environment and particularly the general existence of individuals. When we ask who is or was the most intelligent – Albert Einstein (a theoretical physicist), Delia Smith (a creative cook), or David Beckham (a soccer player) – this depends on the context and values held by a person answering the question. This means our regard for intelligent individuals can be extremely fickle. If Einstein's theories were overturned, Delia Smith's cookery poisoned a restaurant full of people, or David Beckham broke his leg, suddenly we might not regard them as being anywhere near as intelligent as before, yet they would not have changed in themselves.

Just as we apply subjective intelligence between groups of humans (with one group assuming that a particular feature indicates intelligence while another group does not think so), we tend to do the same between different creatures and even machines such as robots. As humans we feel that what we do, and how we live, is of considerable value and cannot be bettered. As a result it is difficult for us to conceive of some other creature being better than we are, in an all-round sense, and as a consequence, being more powerful. We tend to relate everything, including intelligence, to a human value set according to human physical abilities. It could be thought that for another species to surpass humans, individuals in that species would have to be better than humans in absolutely everything we do. This is simply not so.

COMPARING INTELLIGENCE

As we have seen, humans do not surpass all animals, insects and machines in everything they do. In fact there are many things that individuals in each of those groupings can do, that humans simply cannot do, due to physical or mental limitations. In short, one species does not have to be better than another species, in all aspects of that species' existence, for it to be more successful and possibly more powerful. So robots of the future do not have to be better than humans in all aspects of our physical and mental abilities, particularly human intelligence, for them to be more successful. It is the general, all-round ability that is most important.

Humans, other animals and insects have all evolved as a balanced whole, with their physical and mental processes working in harmony. An individual's intelligence is an integral part of their make-up, and is related to their physical abilities when fully operational. This overall intelligence has been referred to as an individual's resultant intelligence. For all creatures there exists a relevant subjective intelligence which applies to their species, and still further, to a particular subject, or group, within the species. So too with machines. For each robot or computer, a subjective intelligence applies which is relevant to that particular robot group.

The fact that mental and physical abilities are quite different between species means it becomes difficult to relate the performance of an individual in one species to that of an individual in another species, other than in terms of particular tasks or feats. For example, we could consider the maximum, unaided, speed of a cheetah, human, spider and car and rank the contenders accordingly, but the results would apply only to speed. Similarly, we could rank humans, computers, chimps and spiders in terms of their abilities at chess. Although this presents a problem (in that it is physically difficult for spiders to play chess), I imagine such a ranking can nevertheless be made, just as it can with the same group in terms of their web-making abilities.

Comparing the intelligence of individuals in different species is therefore almost meaningless, except in terms of undertaking specific tasks. Indeed the same is true when comparing individuals within a species. For example, if one computer beats another computer at chess we should not conclude that it is also better at weather forecasting and missile flight control. So too with humans. If one human is better than another at theoretical physics, it means just that, and nothing more.

In the past, we have attempted to measure the extremely complex, multi-dimensional entity that is intelligence as a one-dimensional, single value (namely IQ). Clearly this is not appropriate for individuals in any species. The intelligence of an individual is a result of their mental processing; it has many different attributes, it is multi-dimensional. It can be graphically represented as a point in a hypersphere (the hypersphere of intelligence), where each axis represents an attribute. If we indicate this simply as a single number then we are falling into one of the following traps: ignoring all but a few dimensions; taking a rough average of those remaining; or merely finding the magnitude of the point from the origin. It is not that intelligence has two, three, or even seven different attributes. It has, potentially, an infinite number.

Having said this, we humans still appear to hold IQ testing in high esteem. When a single number is available it becomes quite straightforward to see how an individual's other behaviours affect that single number. In other words, if a person does A will this affect their IQ more or less than if they do B? Surprising though they were, the results of the IQ experiment described in Chapter 7 merely indicated an improvement in performance on a specific test, over a short period of time, in response to particular behaviours, by a group of 120 narrowly defined individuals. They are, however, particularly relevant to students and other exam-takers in terms of indicating what might be a good pre-exam strategy.

Some of the behaviours in the experiment involved physical activity, whereas others were more focused on the mental side. The link between mental and physical aspects is clearly critical. As the old expression 'sound in mind, sound in body' implies, both are extremely important. So much so that it is worth remembering to take regular mental exercise just as much as regular physical exercise. In the same way as people get physically flabby and sluggish if they don't take regular exercise, so they can also get mentally flabby and sluggish if they do not exercise their brains.

NATURE AND NURTURE

With human individuals we can see considerable physical differences – short and tall, strong and weak, thin and fat, and so on. In each case physical ability can be improved by training but overall characteristics are partly due to initial programed genetic abilities and partly due to their enhancement by training. The same appears to be true of our minds. After all, the brain is itself a physical organ, which must be subject to genetic differences. The idea that humans are physically different in all aspects, except that our brains are all identical, is too silly to consider seriously. Intellectual performance can obviously be altered by training and stimulation. Intelligence must therefore be partly due to nature and part to nurture.

Some people like to speculate on how much of our intelligence is down to nurture and how much to nature. In reality we do not know, and it probably differs considerably between individuals. Asking how much of a weight-lifter's ability is down to genes and how much to training is probably pointless – there is no correct answer to the question. The problem is even more intractable when it comes to an individual's intelligence.

Throughout history, attempts have been made to nail down links between intelligence and one factor or another. For example, intelligence has been linked with social standing, wealth and education. The truth is that all these factors and many more, are linked together in a feedback loop. One thing leads to another, which leads to another, until we are back where we started from. For instance, poverty in a group is not removed by simply giving the group money. Rather, it requires a whole package of measures including technology, sanitation, etc, with education being perhaps the most important of all.

By changing a major parameter within this 'intelligence loop' on a permanent basis, the steady-state position can be changed. It is often the case that poor, working-class, less well-educated, socially deprived individuals have more children than their upper-class, affluent, well-educated counterparts. In India this is particularly true at the moment. If intelligence does have any link with any of these factors, and there are many indications that it is, on average, linked to all of them, then there is a downward pull on the average level of intelligence in India at the present time.

Meanwhile, in China, restricting families to one child has had the effect of creating a profound upward pull on the average level of intelligence for exactly the same reasons. Not only this but families have more money to spend on their one child and the state has more money to spend on better schooling – all positive effects within a feedback loop.

EVOLVING INTELLIGENCE

In each society, indeed within each species, the average intelligence changes as that species evolves. In a one-dimensional, IQ, sense it can be said that the mean IQ level is changing. In terms of the multi-dimensional hypersphere of intelligence, it is the origin or central point of the hypersphere that moves (it being noted that each species has its own hypersphere, with dimensions indicative of intelligence within that species, i.e. subjective to that species). While, from an evolutionary viewpoint at least, some 'improvement' in intelligence should be occurring, it is more than likely that the mean/centre is shifting as a species adapts, becoming more capable in some aspects but perhaps less capable in others. At present, as human intelligence adapts to cope with an increasingly technological world, so our computer interaction may improve but our basic numeracy may get worse because we do not need to get involved with numerical calculation in the same way we used to. Just as our keyboard skills improve as we rely more on keyboards, so we can reasonably expect our handwriting skills to get worse.

It is natural for the intelligence of individuals within a species to evolve. If the environment changes, so organisms within that environment will need to adapt. Those that do not adapt quickly enough may well perish. Such factors can be clearly seen in action in modern human societies. An individual is educated, for example, and can then obtain employment. While in employment it is better for them to continue learning to enable them to adapt. Firstly, this allows them to target better employment opportunities when they arise. And secondly, if they do not adapt they are likely to have their employment terminated as their company must itself adapt. It may then be difficult for them to find another position in the employment market. They may ultimately perish.

Organisms can themselves change their environment or make a new environment. As humans, we are currently changing our environment in order to extend our capabilities. However, we are failing to take the long-term consequences into account. The environment is being changed, by ourselves, from one that we are better suited to, into one that we are not so well suited to. For example, far more information is now being generated, than any human can, on their own, hope to deal with. So the big question is: how quickly can we adapt to this new environment? Or will other species, machines, always be better suited to the environment we are creating?

A MACHINE'S HYPERSPHERE

Even machines have a hypersphere of intelligence. But when a machine is designed with one task in mind, with intelligence in one aspect, then essentially it can be looked at in terms of its intelligence as a uni-dimensional measure. When we compare the intelligence of a human with that of a machine, we are then comparing one dimension of the multi-dimensional human hypersphere with the one, and only one, dimension of that machine. The machine may well out-perform the human in that one dimension (such as chess) but be unable to compete in any other dimension whatsoever. If that one dimension is not of central importance in life, and that machine does not compete with humans in any other aspect, then it would be largely subservient to us.

It is, though, quite possible for machines to have a complex multi-dimensional hypersphere of their own, particularly when we consider a machine network, which can physically sense the outside world and affect it via actuators of some kind. Only when a machine networked intelligence can out-perform human intelligence in a number of important dimensions, and not until then, will humans have a potential problem to deal with. Unfortunately it is not easy for humans to identify the important dimensions of intelligence. Essentially this takes us back to the question of what exactly consti-tutes intelligence. In particular, we need to know which features of intelligence are important in the society and culture in which we presently live.

SEX AND SUCCESS

As we saw with insects, one critical factor in an individual's make-up is the ability to produce offspring. The first point to note here is the use of the word 'production' and not 'reproduction'. As far as I am aware, just about all creatures, humans included, produce offspring; they do not, except for cloning, reproduce. Machines obviously produce other machines. However, whilst animals are restricted to the production of offspring solely of the same species, machines have the ability to produce other machines very different from themselves. This characteristic is shared by humans who can also produce machines very different from themselves.

Sex (and the selective production of offspring) plays a vital role in the evolution and success of all creatures. Interestingly, it has been found that after having sexual intercourse the brain of a human shrinks, albeit slightly. This is presumably due to the transference of blood from the brain to certain other parts of the body. In a study on nematode roundworms[2] it was found that, on average, the worms lived 60 per cent longer when their sexual apparatus had been removed. But what is the point of their existence with no apparatus?

It could be argued that the whole purpose of life for an individual is to produce offspring, thereby continuing, and evolving, the species. This would lead us to conclude that the aspect of intelligence which allows them to succeed in producing offspring must be very important. In human terms, this currently means taking part in a successful heterosexual relationship.

INHERENT VERSUS RESULTANT INTELLIGENCE

Producing offspring is, however, merely the first step. Starting those offspring off on a successful life is also vital, thereby helping the lineage to have a greater chance of succeeding in the future. Hence, from the creature (non-machine) world, we can conclude that those who produce offspring that are in turn successful, have, from a species viewpoint, achieved success in themselves. The physical and mental conditions that have allowed them to do that are of paramount importance, particularly their intelligence. We could therefore argue that the most important aspect of intelligence is that which facilitates successful life, particularly that which causes an individual to assist in producing successful offspring, thereby helping its species progress on the evolutionary ladder.

We know that resultant intelligence (that which actually has an effect and can be measured in some way) is important. Yet each individual also has an inherent intelligence, which can be described as their brain operating in stand-alone mode (its unrealised potential). Resultant intelligence requires physical sensors, such as eyes and ears in humans, and physical actuators, such as hands and legs. A blind person's inherent intelligence is not necessarily affected, whereas the resultant intelligence – in terms of responding to visual stimulus – is blatantly affected. If, however, a visual system (incorporating operational eyes) is subsequently linked to the brain, then, as long as the inherent intelligence has not been affected, it may well be possible to considerably upgrade their resultant intelligence.

The whole concept of inherent intelligence is also important for individual humans suffering from conditions such as cerebral palsy or autism. It is reported that 10 per cent of those with autism have special abilities, these individuals sometimes being referred to as *savants*. My own feeling is that it may well be that *all* people with autism have special abilities. It is just that, for the other 90 per cent, we have been unable to convert their inherent intelligence into a resultant intelligence that is in any way recognisable.

When we consider machines, the concepts of inherent intelligence and resultant intelligence still hold true. Inherent intelligence effectively depends on the central processing unit of the computer, whereas the resultant intelligence of a machine depends on how it senses the world. The inherent intelligence is therefore most critical, because, by adding on sensors and actuators, we can give the being a different resultant intelligence. For example, we should not say a machine is not intelligent if it cannot make a cup of coffee, when it does not have the physical ability to make a cup of coffee. Exactly the same argument is true for humans.

In twenty to thirty years the inherent intelligence of humans will be roughly similar to what we have at present, while computers will almost certainly have outstripped us. The human brain's 100 billion highly connected cells will have been surpassed by machines with more cells, more densely connected together and linked directly into a high performance network.

IQ VERSUS HYPERSPHERE

With different species the only realistic way we can compare intelligence is in terms of gladiator-style contests in an intellectual arena. Internal, philosophical issues, such as consciousness, do not count for anything in this arena.

As we know, the intelligence of each species is subjective to that species, and depends on physical characteristics (such as how the world is sensed) as much as on inherent mental aspects. As a result it is perhaps impossible to achieve an objective test of intelligence. Each test of intelligence would need to be different for each species, for each collective group within a species, and ultimately for each individual within a species. With machines this is quite clear – testing the intelligence of a kettle against that of a chess-playing computer is obviously meaningless. Yet in human terms that is exactly what has been done in the past, and is still being done now, in the form of IQ tests.

With machines, playing chess could be defined as something requiring intelligence; boiling water not. The chess-playing computer, we could then conclude, is more intelligent than the kettle. But is this not a stupid statement? So too, with humans, if we say that reading Latin requires high intelligence whereas playing soccer does not, we might come to a similar, stupid conclusion. Clearly these questions are very subjective and culturally biased.

Even when we do consider a uniform group and apply some sort of test we may find that all sorts of factors affect the results obtained. For example, in Chapter 7 we saw how different nutritional intakes and activities immediately affected how individuals within a group were characterised and regarded. The experiment showed how the measure taken (the IQ score) could be directly changed by each individual's bodily state. If an individual can affect a measure, such as that from an IQ test, simply by what they do prior to the test then habitually carrying out certain activities (such as in learning) obviously will have a longer-lasting effect – whether positive or negative!

One key aim of this book is to consider the intelligence of an individual not in terms of a single (IQ) number, but rather as a complex, multi-dimensional facility. Different individuals can perform intellectually better or worse on each of these facilities. The fact that an individual performs well on one aspect, such as music or soccer, gives little or no indication as to whether that individual performs well on others, except when the different facilities are closely related. Hence a Greek scholar may also perform well as a Latin scholar, as the two characteristics are related. Similarly a good soccer player may also turn out to be a good volleyball player.

Using the hypersphere model, each individual's intelligence can be characterised by how they perform on the wide range of axes which represent the different aspects of their intelligence. Rather than being represented by a single number (IQ), an individual's intelligence can thus be measured with a whole collection of numbers – a score for maths, a score for music, a score for art, motorcycle maintenance, etc. Graphically this can be represented by a point in the hypersphere. So how do we go about measuring this point for each individual? For humans an argument would ensue as to which axes should be included and which not. For instance, is skill at motorcycle maintenance any indication of intelligence? What about artistic ability? Is knowledge of the geography of Iceland more or less important than the ability to juggle three balls in the air? Once again we come back to the problem of subjectivity.

Nevertheless, our quest to find the truth behind intelligence can come to a conclusion. What we *do* know is that intelligence relates to the resultant and inherent mental processing of an individual. What is regarded as an important aspect of intelligence, and what is regarded as not so important, is subjective to individuals.

As far as IQ tests are concerned, these are partly indicative of a small range of an individual human's ability. It appears that they may also give a rough indication of that individual's performance in some school or academic subjects. This is probably true because of the correlation between IQ tests and school-type exams. However, regular good performance on IQ tests only tells us that the individual is good at such tests. It is certainly not a measure of their intelligence in general. It does not give any indication of their ability to whistle 'Colonel Bogey' or fly an aeroplane, as these are not skills that are generally looked for in IQ tests.

Even with such tests we have seen that certain activities alter the results obtained. For example, drinking coffee improves an IQ test score. But this does not mean that drinking coffee improves intelligence in general; nor does it necessarily mean that drinking litres of coffee will make you super-intelligent. In fact it is often unclear what is a good experience or activity and what is a bad one, from an intelligence perspective. Contradictory information or activities can assist intelligence or hinder it, as we have found in experimenting with our robots.

The Struggle for Survival

It is clear that if robots of the future are more intelligent than humans, we may have a big problem. How, though, can we know this, unless we understand what intelligence is? As we have seen, we have a rough idea of what it is in humans but, due to cultural pressures, a great deal of subjectivity creeps in; it is only natural that it does. With robots it is very difficult to judge. It is their resultant intelligence that is important, as far as humans are concerned, and this depends on the way they sense the world. But how can we assess the importance of understanding the world in terms of x-rays or ultraviolet light, when these are not the ways that we, as humans, have evolved to understand the world?

The fact is that the flexibility and potential power of machine intelligence far surpasses that of humans. It may be comforting to say that machines, or any other creatures for that matter, are not like us, particularly in terms of our intelligence, therefore they will always be inferior to us. It is reassuring to conclude that, if machines are not conscious as humans are, then we have nothing to worry about. But this is pure Hollywood – it is not science.

If we can draw out a universal measure that relates to intelligence then surely it must be success. While it can certainly be questioned whether 'civilised man is a being superior to primitive man' in terms of 'fundamental qualities',[3] when a more developed human group has come up against a less developed one, the former has always come out on top. Thus American Indians, Aztecs and Aborigines all lost out to their more 'civilised' conquerors, while innumerable wars have been won by flashes of intelligence – from reflecting the sun off polished shields to radar. Intelligence has gone hand in hand with the more developed, more civilised victors.

In the animal and insect worlds it is the more ingenious creature that wins out, whether this be within a species or between different species. If aliens came to Earth their success or failure would depend on whether or not they could out-think humans. Whilst only one aspect of intelligence is required for one individual to succeed over another in a chess match, or in an exam or in a financial deal, when it comes to life in general then intelligence in all its multidimensionality comes into play. So, if a one-line definition of intelligence is called for, we could say: 'Intelligence is the variety of mental processes that act together to make up those necessary for life.'

When we compare the important aspects of intelligence between species, it is those which can allow one species to dominate and exert power over other species that are of prime importance. In these ways humans have had a charmed existence in relation to many other creatures. But an ability to sense the world in a wider variety of ways and on a much more complex level, to think much more quickly and to have a better understanding of the feedback loops that exist in life; all these capabilities give machines of the future a tremendous potential advantage over humans. It is, however, humans who are instigating and initially developing such machines. The sword of life is intelligence. As we have lived by the sword with other creatures, so we will die by the sword in the hands of robots.

BIBLIOGRAPHY
AND RESOURCES

Aiello, L.C., 'Terrestriality, Bipedalism and the Origins of Language'. *Proceedings of the British Academy* 88 (Evolution of Social Behaviour Patterns) (1996) 269–289.

Aitchison, J., *The Seeds of Speech: Language Origin and Evolution.* Cambridge, Cambridge University Press (1996).

Aleksander, I., *Impossible Minds*, Imperial College Press, (1996).

Baines, J. and Malek, J., *Atlas of Ancient Egypt*, Oxford, Elsevier (1980).

Balfour, D. and Balfour, S., *African Elephants: A Celebration of Majesty.* Cape Town, Struik Publishers Ltd (1997).

Batchelor, B. G. and Waltz, F. M., *Interactive Image Processing for Machine Vision*, Springer-Verlag (1993).

Baughman, E. E., *Black Americans: A Psychological Analysis*, New York, Academic Press (1971).

Benton, D. & Roberts, G., 'Effect of Vitamin and Mineral

Supplementation on Intelligence of a Sample of School Children,' *Lancet* (1988) 1: 140–144.

Berkell, D. E., *Autism: Identification, Education and Treatment*, Lawrence Erlbaum Associates, New Jersey and London, (1992).

Bickerton, D., Language and Human Behaviour, London, UCL Press Limited (1995).

Binet, A. and Simon, T., *A Method of Measuring the Development of Young Children*, Lincoln, Illinois, Courier Company (1911).

Bjorklund, D. F., *Children's Thinking: Developmental Function and Individual Differences*, California, Brooks/Cole Publishing Company (1989).

Blagg, N., *Can We Teach Intelligence? A Comprehensive Evaluation of Feuerstein's Instrumental Enrichment Program*, New Jersey, Lawrence Erlbaum Associates Inc (1991).

Boden, M. A. 'Precis of The Creative Mind: Myths and Mechanisms', *Behavioural and Brain Sciences*, (1994) 17: 519–570.

Boesch, C. 'The Emergence of Cultures Among Wild Chimpanzees', *Proceedings of the British Academy* (1996) 88 (Evolution of Social Behavioural Patterns): 251–268.

Brigham, C. C. 'Intelligence Tests of Immigrant Groups'. *Psychological Review* (1930) 37: 158–165.

Burt, C. 'Experimental Tests of General Intelligence', *The British Journal of Psychology* (1909), 3: 94–177.

Byrne, R. W. and Whiten, A., *Machiavellian Intelligence*, Clarendon Press, Oxford (1988).

Calvin, W. H., *How Brains Think: Evolving Intelligence, Then and Now*, London, Weidenfield and Nicolson (1996).

Calvin, W. H., 'The Emergence of Intelligence', *Scientific American Presents*, (1998) 9: 44–52.

Candland, D. K., *Feral Children and Clever Animals: Reflections on Human Nature*, Oxford, Oxford University Press (1993).

Coe, M. D., *Mexico: From the Olmecs to the Aztecs*, London, Thames and Hudson (1994).

Colombo, J. *Infant Cognition: Predicting Later Intellectual Functioning*, California, SAGE Publications (1993).

Conroy, G. C., *Primate Evolution*, New York, W. W. Norton and Company (1990).

Davies, R., *Prodigies: Exceptional Childhoods and Supernormal Powers*, London, Aquarian Press (1992a).

Davies, R., *Child Prodigies and Exceptional Early Achievers*, London, Harvester Wheatsheaf (1992b).

Deacon, T., *The Symbolic Species: The Co-evolution of Language and the Human Brain*, England, Penguin Books (1997).

Devlin, B., Daniels, M. et al., *The Heritability of IQ'*, *Nature* (1997), **388** (6639): 468–471.

Dilke, O. A. W., *The Ancient Romans: How They Lived and Worked*, Newton Abbot, David and Charles (1975).

Dunbar, R. I. M., *Primate Social Systems*, London and Sydney, Croom Helm (1988).

Dunbar, R. I. M., 'Coevolution of Neocortical Size, Group Size and Language in Humans', *Behavioural and Brain Sciences* (1993), **16**: 681–735.

Dunbar, R. I. M., 'Determinants of Group Size in Primates: A General Model,' *Proceedings of the British Academy* **88** (Evolution of Social Behaviour Patterns) (1996a): 33–57.

Dunbar, R., *Grooming, Gossip and the Evolution of Language*, London and Boston, Faber and Faber (1996b).

Eberhard, W. G., 'Effects of Orb-Web Geometry on Prey Interception and Retention', *Spiders: Webs, Behaviour, and Evolution*, W. A. Shear, California, Stanford University Press (1986): 70–100.

Eysenck, H. *Know Your Own I.Q.*, Penguin (1968).

Fancher, R. E., *The Intelligence Men: Makers of the IQ Controversy*, New York, W. W. Norton and Company (1985).

Firth, U., *Autism: Explaining the Enigma*, Oxford, Blackwells (1989).

Fodor, J. A., 'Precis of the Modularity of Mind', *The Behavioural and Brain Sciences* (1985), 8: 1–42.

Foley, R. A., 'An Evolutionary and Chronological Framework for Human Social Behaviour', *Proceedings of the British Academy* (1996), **88** (Evolution of Social Behaviour Problems): 95–117.

Fossey, D., *Gorillas in the Mist*, London, Hodder and Stoughton (1983).

Gale, C. R. and C. N. Martyn, 'Breastfeeding, Dummy Use and Adult Intelligence', *The Lancet* (1996), 347: 1072–1075.

Gardner, H., 'A Multiplicity of Intelligences', *Scientific American Presents* (1998), 9: 18–24.

Garis, H. D., International Conference on Neural Nets and Genetic Algorithms, Ales, France, Springer-Verlag (1995).

Gibson, W., *Mona Lisa Overdrive*, Voyager (1995).

Gillham, J., *Journal of Corrective Social Psychology* (1975) 21, 13–25.

Goleman, D., *Emotional Intelligence: Why It Can Matter More Than IQ*, London, Bloomsbury (1995).

Goodall, J., *Through a Window: Thirty Years with the Chimpanzees of Gombe*, London, Penguin Books.

Goodman, L. J. and Fisher, R. C., *The Behaviour and Physiology of Bees*, CAB International, Wallingford, (1991).

Gould, J. L. and Gould, C. G., *The Honey Bee*, New York, Scientific American Library, (1988).

Gould, J. L. and Gould, C. G., 'Reasoning in Animals', *Scientific American Presents* (1998), 9: 52–60.

Gould, S. J., *The Mismeasure of Man: Revised and Expanded Edition*, England, Pengin Books (1996).

Greenfield, S., *The Human Brain: A Guided Tour*, London, Weidenfeld and Nicolson (1997).

Greenfield, S. A., *The Private Life of the Brain*, London, Penguin, (2000).

Griffin, D. R., *Bird Migration*, New York, Dover, (1974).

Griffiths, S., *Predictions*, Oxford, Oxford University Press, (1999).

Hamilton, R., Ed., *Father Bernabe Cobo – Inca Religion and Customs*, Austin, University of Texas Press, (1990).

Hammond, J., Converse, T. M. et al., 'The Stabilisation of Environments', *Artificial Intelligence*, (1995), **72**: 305–327.

Hauser, M. D., *The Evolution of Communication*, London, The MIT Press, (1996).

Haynes, G., *Mammoths, Mastodonts and Elephants*, Cambridge, Cambridge University Press, (1991).

Hearnshaw, L. S., *Cyril Burt Psychologist*, Kent, Hodder and Stoughton, (1979).

Hebb, D. O., *The Organisation of Behaviour: A Neurophysical Theory*, New York, John Wiley and Sons (1949).

Hedgepeth, W., *The Hog Book*, Athens and London, The University of Georgia Press, (1998).

Hernstein, R. J. and Loveland, D. H., "Complex Visual Concepts in Pigeons', *Science* (1964), 146, 549–551.

Herrnstein, R. and Murray, C., *The Bell Curve: Intelligence and Class Structure in American Life*, New York, Free Press Paperbacks, (1994).

Hirschfeld, L. A. and German, S. A., *Mapping the Mind: Domain Specificity in Cognition and Culture*, Cambridge University Press, Cambridge, (1994).

Hofstadter, D. R. and Dennett, D. G., *In the Mind's I*, Penguin, Harmondsworth, (1981).

Holldobler, B. and Wilson, E. O., *The Ants*, Springer-Verlag, (1990).

Howe, M. J. A., *The Origins of Exceptional Abilities*, Oxford, Blackwells, (1990).

Howe, M. L. and Pasnak, R., *Emerging Themes in Cognitive Development*, New York, Springer-Verlag, (1993).

Jackendoff, R., *Patterns in the Mind: Language and Human Nature*, London, Harvester Wheatsheaf (1993).

Jensen, A. R., *Educational Differences,* London, Methuen and Co Ltd, (1973).

Jerison, H. J., 'The Perceptual World of Dolphins', *Dolphin Cognition and Behaviour: A Comparative Approach,* Schusterman, R. J., Thomas, J. A., and Wood, F. G., London, Lawrence Erlbaum Associates, (1986): 141–166.

Johanson, D. and Edgar, B., *From Lucy to Language,* London, Weidenfeld and Nicolson, (1996).

Johnson, M. H., *Brain Development and Cognition: A Reader,* Oxford, Blackwell, (1993).

Koluchova, J., 'Severe Deprivation in Twins: A Case Study', *Journal of Child Psychology and Psychiatry*, (1972), **13**: 107–114.

Larson, E. J., *Summer for the Gods*, Harvard University Press (1998).

Leatherwood, S. and Reeves, R. R., *The Bottlenose Dolphin*, San Diego, Academic Press Inc, (1990).

Lewin, R., *Human Evolution: An Illustrated Introduction,* Boston, Blackwell Scientific Publications, (1993).

Lewis, M., *Origins of Intelligence: Infancy and Early Childhood,* New York, Plenum Press, (1983).

Lifton, R. J., *The Nazi Doctors: A Study of the Psychology of Evil,* London, Macmillan, (1986).

Lindbergh, C., 'Is Civilisation Progress?', *Readers Digest*, (1964): 67–74.

Loehlin, C., Gardner, L. et al., *Race Differences in Intelligence*, San Francisco, W. H. Freeman, (1975).

Marten, K. and Psarakos, S. http//www.planet_hawaii.com/earthtrust. delbook.html.

Martyn, C. N., Gale, C. R. et al., 'Growth in Utero and Cognitive Function in Adult Life: Follow Up Study of People Born Between 1920 and 1943', *The British Medical Journal*, (1996), **312**: 1393–1396.

Masson, J. and McCarthy, S., *When Elephants Weep: The Emotional Lives of Animals,* London, Vintage, (1996).

Matlin, M., *The Psychology of Women,* USA, Holt, Rinehart and Winston, Inc., (1987).

McGrew, W. C., *Chimpanzee Material Culture: Implications for Human Evolution.* Cambridge, Cambridge University Press, (1992).

Meadows, S., *The Child as Thinker: The Development and Acquisition of Cognition in Childhood,* London and New York, Routledge, (1993).

Meeks-Gardner, J. M. and Grantham-McGregor, S. M., 'Physical Activity, Undernutrition and Child Development', *Proceedings of the Nutrition Society,* (1994), **53**: 443–456.

Mellars, P. and Stringer, C., *The Human Revolution: Behavioural and Biological Perspectives on the Origins of Modern Humans,* Edinburgh, Edinburgh University Press, (1989).

Mellars, P., 'The Emergence of Biologically Modern Populations in Europe: A Social and Cognitive "Revolution"?', *Proceedings of the British Academy,* (1996), **88** (Evolution of Social Behavioural Patterns): 179–201.

Mellars, P. and Gibson, K., *Modelling the Early Human Mind,* Cambridge, (1996).

Michael, J. S., 'A New Look at Morton's Craniological Research', *Current Anthropology,* (1988), **29**: 349–354.

Miller, G. A. and Buckhout, R., *Psychology: The Science of Mental Life,* New York, Harper and Row, (1973).

Mira, M., Alperstein G. et al., 'Haem Iron Intake in 12–36 Month Old Children Depleted in Iron: Case-Control Study', *The British Medical Journal,* (1996), **312**: 881–883.

Mithen, S., *The Prehistory of the Mind,* London, Thames and Hudson, (1996).

Mithen, S., 'The Early Prehistory of Human Social Behaviour: Issues of Archaeological Inference and Cognitive Evolution', *Proceedings of the British Academy,* (1996), **88** (Evolution of Social Behaviour Patterns): 145–177.

Moffat, W. M. and Moffat, H. S. M. A. J. M., 'Transmission of Vibration in a Spider's Web', *Spiders: Webs, Behaviour and Evolution*, W. A. Shear, California, Stanford University Press, (1986): 49–69.

Moir, A. and Jessel, D., *Brainsex: The Real Differences Between Men and Women*, London, Mandarin Paperbacks, (1989).

Nagel, T., 'What is it Like to be a Bat?', *Philosophical Review*, (1974) 83: 435–450.

Newman, H. H., Freeman, F. N. et al., *Twins: A Study of Heredity and Environment*, Chicago, University of Chicago Press, (1937).

Nitecki, M. H. and Nitecki, D. V., *Origins of Anatomically Modern Humans*, Plenum Press, New York and London, (1994).

O'Connor, N., and Hermelin, B., 'Low Intelligence and Special Abilities', *Journal of Child Psychology and Psychiatry*, (1988) 29: 391–396.

Olley, J. G., 'Autism: Historical Overview, Definition and Characteristics', *Autism: Identification, Education and Treatment*, D. E. Berkell, New Jersey and London, Lawrence Erlbaum Associates, (1992): 3–20.

Olson, D. R. and Torrance, N. (eds), *The Handbook of Education and Human Development*, Cambridge, Blackwell (1996).

Orquera, L. A., 'Specialisation and the Middle/Upper Palaeolithic Transition', *Current Anthropology*, (1984), 25: 73–98.

Penrose, R., *Shadows of the Mind*, Oxford, Oxford University Press, (1994).

Pepperberg, I. M., 'Evidence for Conceptual Quantitative Abilities in the African Grey Parrot: Labelling of Cardinal Sets', *Ethology*, (1987) 75: 37–61.

Pepperberg, I. M., 'Cognition in an African Gray Parrot (*Psittacus erithacus*): Further Evidence for Comprehension of Categories and Labels', *Journal of Comparative Psychology*, (1990), 104 (1): 41–52.

Pinker, S., *The Language Instinct: The New Science of Language and Mind*, London, Penguin Books (1994).

Pocock, S. J., Smith, M. et al., 'Environmental Lead and Children's Intelligence: A Systematic Review of the Epidemiological Evidence', *The British Medical Journal*, (1994), **309**: 1189–97.

Preston, J. and Bishop, J. M., *Views Into the Chinese Room*, Oxford University Press, 2000.

Preston-Mafham, R., *The Book of Spiders and Scorpions*, New York, Crescent Books, (1991).

Pyror, K., and Norris, K. S., *Dolphin Societies: Discoveries and Puzzles*, London, University of California Press (1998).

Rach, J., *Why Does My Bird Do That?*, New York, Howell Book House, (1998).

Reuters (London) @http://dailynews.yahoo.com/h/nm//20000501/od/future-l.htm//May (2000).

Richardson, K., *Understanding Intelligence*, Milton Keynes, Open University Press, (1991).

Riechert, S. E. and Gillespie, R. G., 'Habitat Choice and Utilisation in Web-Building Spiders', *Spiders, Behaviour and Evolution*, W. A. Shear, California, Stanford University Press, (1986), 23–48.

Rodgers, P. J. and Lloyd, H. M., 'Nutrition and Mental Performance', *Proceedings of the Nutrition Society*, (1994), **53**: 443–456.

Romanes, G. J., *Animal Intelligence*, (1888).

Sacks, O., *An Anthropologist on Mars*, Picador, (1995).

Schaik, C. P. V., 'Social Evolution in Primates: The Role of Ecological Factors and Male Behaviour', *Proceedings of the British Academy*, (1996), **88** (Evolution of Social Behaviour Patterns in Primates and Man: A Joint Discussion Meeting of the Royal Society and the British Academy): 9–31.

Scott-Berg, A., *Lindbergh*, Basingstoke, Macmillan, 1998.

Searle, J. R., *The Mystery of Consciousness*, New York, New York Review Book, (1997).

Smith, N., and Tsimpli, I., *The Mind of the Savant: Language Learning and Modularity*, Oxford, Blackwells, (1995).

Spearman, C., 'General Intelligence: Objectively Determined and Measured', *The American Journal of Psychology*, (1904), **15**: 201–293.

Spearman, C., *The Nature of Intelligence and the Principles of Cognition*, London, Macmillan and Co., (1923).

Stafford-Clark, D., *Psychiatry Today*, London, Pelican, (1961).

Sternberg, R. J., 'How Intelligent is Intelligence Testing?', *Scientific American Presents*, (1998), **9**: 12–18.

Sternberg, R. J., and Berg, C. A., *Intellectual Development*, Cambridge University Press, Cambridge, (1992).

Stringer, C. and Gamble, C., *In Search of the Neanderthals*, Thames and Hudson, (1993).

Strouhal, E., *Life of the Ancient Egyptians*, Liverpool, Liverpool University Press, (1997).

Tattersall, I., *The Fossil Trail: How We Know What We Think We Know About Human Evolution*, New York and Oxford, Oxford University Press, (1995).

Teachers, J. A. O. C., *The World of Athens: An Introduction to Classical Athenian Culture*, Cambridge, Cambridge University Press, (1984).

Tong, S., Baghurst, P. et al., 'Lifetime Exposure to Environmental Lead and Children's Intelligence at 11–13 Years: Port Pirie Cohort Study', *The British Medical Journal*, (1996), **312**: 1569–1575.

Townsend, R. F., *The Aztecs*, London, Thames and Hudson, (1992).

Tustin, F., *Autistic States in Children*, London, Routledge and Kegan Paul, (1981).

Underhill, L. E. and Littlefield, D. F., Eds., *Hamlin Garland's Observations on the American Indian 1895–1905*, Arizona, University of Arizona Press, (1976).

Vernon, P. E., *Intelligence: Heredity and Environment*, San Francisco, W. H. Freeman and Company, (1979).

Vries, G. J. D., *Sex Differences in the Brain*, Elsevier Science Publications, Oxford, (1984).

Waal, F. D., *Chimpanzee Politics: Power and Sex Among Apes*, London, Jonathan Cape Ltd, (1982).

Warwick, K., 'I, Robot.', *Wired*, (2000), 8: 144–151.

Warwick, K., *March of the Machines*, Century, (1997).

Watson, P., *Twins: An Investigation into the Strange Coincidences in the Lives of Separate Twins*, London, Hutchinson, (1981).

White, J. M., *Everyday Life of the North American Indians*, New York, Dorset Press, (1979).

White, R., 'Rethinking the Middle/Upper Palaeolithic Transition', *Current Anthropology*, (1982), **23**: 169–192.

Witt, P. N. and Rouner, J. S., *Spider Communication: Mechanisms and Ecological Significance,* Princeton University Press, Princeton, (1982).

Wood, B., 'Early Homo: How Many Species?', *Species, Species Concepts and Primate Evolution*, W. H., Kimbel and L. B. Martin, New York and London, Plenum Press, (1993): 485–522.

Wright, R., *Stolen Continents: The Indian Story*, London, Pimlico, (1992).

Yam, P., 'Intelligence Considered', *Scientific American Presents*, (1998), **9**: 6–12.

Znigg, R., 'Feral man and Extreme Cases of Isolation', *The American Journal of Psychology*, (1940), **LIII**: 487–517.

NOTES BY CHAPTER

Chapter 1

1 *Daily Mail*, 28 October 1999.
2 Goleman (1995).
3 Eysenck (1968), p. 104.

Chapter 2

1 Lewin (1993).
2 Mithen (1996) and Johanson (1996).
3 Mithen (1996).
4 Foley and Lee (1996) in Foley (1996).
5 Rodman and McHenry, in Lewin (1993).
6 Batchelor et al. (1993).
7 White (1979).
8 In Dilke (1975), pp. 155.
9 White (1979).
10 Ibid., pp. 103, 105.
11 Wright (1992).
12 Ibid.
13 Ibid.
14 Strouhal (1997).
15 Ibid.

Chapter 3

1 Dunbar (1996b).
2 Ibid.
3 Ibid.

4 Mithen (1996) and Dunbar (1996b).
5 Aitchison (1996).
6 Dunbar (1996b).
7 Aleksander (1996) and Greenfield (1997).
8 Dunbar (1996a).
9 Pinker (1994).
10 In Aiello (1996).
11 Aiello in Mellars, P. and Gibson, K. (1996).

Chapter 4

1 Richardson (1991).
2 *Macmillan Encyclopaedia* (1995).
3 Spearman (1904), 272.
4 Gould (1996). The revised and expanded edition of *The Mismeasure of Man*, which includes a review of *The Bell Curve*, by Herrnstein and Murray.
5 Hebb (1949) p. 294.
6 Ibid.
7 Hebb (1949) p. 295.
8 Greenfield (1998). Public lecture at University of Reading, Department of Chemistry, on 2 March 1998.
9 All these examples are from Watson (1981).

10 For example the case of the Springer twins is discussed in my last book *March of the Machines* (1997). (The paperback version was titled *In the Mind of the Machine*.)
11 Watson (1981).
12 Fancher (1985).
13 Watson (1981).

Chapter 5
1 Binet and Simon (1911).
2 Jensen (1973).
3 Gould (1996), 193, from Goddard, H. H. (1914), *Feeble-mindedness: its Causes and Consequences*, New York: Macmillan, 561.
4 Gould (1996), p. 194, from Goddard, H. H. (1914), *Feeble-mindedness: its Causes and Consequences*, New York: Macmillan, p. 273.
5 Gould (1996).
6 Ibid.
7 Herrnstein, R. and C. Murray (1994), *The Bell Curve: Intelligence and Class Structure in American Life*, New York: Free Press Paperbacks. This is a highly controversial book which basically deals with intelligence in terms of the nature theory. One of its most controversial statements is that the IQ level of black Americans is lower than that of whites because of genetics; that is blacks are *naturally* less intelligent than whites. This is going back to the ideas of the early 1900s.
8 Gould (1996).
9 In both: Lewis (1983), pp. 14–15 and Gould (1996), p. 230.
10 Gould (1996).
11 Ibid.
12 Ibid, p. 251.
13 Ibid., p. 260. From Brigham, C. C., *A Study of American Intelligence*, (1923), Princeton, Princeton University Press, pp. 209–210.
14 Gould (1996), p. 261.
15 *Macmillan Encyclopaedia* (1995).
16 Penrose (1994).
17 Eysenck (1968).
18 Vernon (1979).

Chapter 6
1 Moir and Jessel (1989).
2 Bayerthal (1911) in Vries (1984), p. 367.
3 Ibid.
4 In Gould (1996).
5 Ibid.
6 David Seaman on *Breakfast with Frost*, BBC1, Sunday 10 May 1998.
7 Herrnstein and Murray (1994).
8 IEEE Spectrum, (1998).
9 Rodgers and Lloyd (1994).
10 Pocock, Smith and Baghurst (1994).
11 Gale and Martyn (1996).
12 Ibid.
13 Herrnstein and Murray (1994).

14 Koluchova (1972).

15 Candland (1993).

16 Ibid.

17 Ibid.

18 Scott-Berg (1998).

19 Herrnstein and Murray (1994).

20 Ibid.

21 Ibid.

22 Loehlin, Gardner and Spuhler (1975).

23 Gould (1996).

24 Ibid.

25 Michael (1988).

Chapter 8

1 Howe (1990).

2 Ibid.

3 Davies (1992a, b).

4 Sacks (1995).

5 Olley (1992), Tustin (1981).

6 Smith and Tsimpli (1995).

Chapter 9

1 Gardner, Torff and Hatch (1996).

Chapter 10

1 Candland (1993).

2 Romanes (1988).

3 Gould and Gould (1998).

4 Stafford-Clark (1961). This refers to Pavlov's experiments, begun in 1889, which demonstrated conditioned and unconditioned reflexes in dogs.

5 Searle (1997).

6 Candland (1993).

7 Ibid., pp. 113–115.

8 Mithen (1996).

9 McGrew (1992).

10 Gould and Gould (1998).

11 Mithen (1996).

12 Gould and Gould (1998).

13 Waal (1988).

14 Ibid.

15 Mithen (1996).

16 McGrew (1992).

17 Gould and Gould (1998).

18 Marten and Psarakos (1995).

19 Jerison (1986).

20 Dunbar (1996b), Leatherwood and Reeves (1990).

21 K. Martin and S. Psarakos (1995). From http://www.planet-hawai.com/earthtrust/delbook.html.

22 Klinowska (1991). From http://www.seaworld.org/bottlenose-dolphin/deathdol.html.

23 'Social Behaviour of Whales' by P. J. from http://sanborn. k12nh.us/HS/whalbt/socbhv.html.

24 Howard (1956) in Rach (1998).

25 Griffin (1974).

26 Herrnstein and Loveland (1964).

27 From http://www.worldkids.net/critters/mammals/pigs.htm.

28 Hedgepeth (1998), p. 111.

29 Hedgepeth (1998).

30 Hedgepeth (1998), p. 157.

31 Masson and McCarthy (1996).

32 Ibid.

Chapter 11

1 Nagel (1974).
2 Sherman (1979). In Holldobler (1990).
3 Halldobler (1990).
4 Jonder (1957). In Holldobler (1990).
5 http://www.msu.edu/user/fcdyer/ research.ntml#Navigation and Spatial Cognition. F. C. Dyer.
6 Lindauer. In Gould (1988).
7 Ibid.
8 Gould (1988).
9 Ibid.

Chapter 12

1 Gers and de Garis (1996) Cambrain: a new model for ATR's cellular automata based artificial brain project, Proceedings of the International Conference on Evaluable Systems, ICE S96.
2 Penrose (1994).
3 Tilden, M., Discovery, Television Program, June 1999.

4 Hofstadler and Dennett (1981).
5 Penrose (1994).
6 Preston, J. and Bishop, J. M. (2000), *Visions Into the Chinese Room*, Oxford University Press.
7 Warwick (1997).
8 Penrose (1994).
9 Searle (1997).
10 Larson, J., (1998).
11 Gibson (1995).

Chapter 13

1 Warwick (1997).
2 Griffiths (1999).
3 Reaters (2000).
4 Warwick (2000).
5 Warwick (1997).

Chapter 14

1 Gillham (1975).
2 Whittell, *The Times*, Saturday 12 June 1999, p. 17.
3 Lindbergh (1964).

INDEX